A Candlelight Ecstasy Romance®

"I THINK WE'RE GETTING TOO CLOSE TOO QUICKLY. WE'VE GOT TO BE SENSIBLE AND CAREFUL BEFORE ONE OF US GETS HURT," CARLY SAID.

"You're too late, Carly," Matt replied.

"Stop, Matt. Don't make this more difficult than it is. I love being with you but I think we have to defuse some of the intensity between us. I have a business to get off the ground and it means everything to me right now. It requires a lot more of my energy and time than I've been able to give it recently."

Matt's eyes narrowed. "Because of me?"

Carly nodded.

"Then we'll just have to spend more days like today—working side by side at the store. One down. What other problems do you envision in our future?"

"Oh, Matt!" Carly cried in exasperation. "Don't you see? I'm just not ready for a serious relationship that will inevitably include commitments and disappointments and responsibilities."

CANDLELIGHT ECSTASY ROMANCES®

SKY GYPSY

Natalie Stone

A CANDLELIGHT ECSTASY ROMANCE®

Published by
Dell Publishing Co., Inc.
1 Dag Hammarskjold Plaza
New York, New York 10017

Dell ® TM 681510, Dell Publishing Co., Inc.
Candlelight Ecstasy Romance®, 1,203,540, is a registered
trademark of Dell Publishing Co., Inc., New York, New York.

ISBN: 0-440-17809-6

Printed in the United States of America
First printing—April 1985

To our five terrific kids—
Erica and Chris
Todd, Aria, and Danny
with lots of love

To Our Readers:

We have been delighted with your enthusiastic response to Candlelight Ecstasy Romances®, and we thank you for the interest you have shown in this exciting series.

In the upcoming months we will continue to present the distinctive, sensuous love stories you have come to expect only from Ecstasy. We look forward to bringing you many more books from your favorite authors and also the very finest work from new authors of contemporary romantic fiction.

As always, we are striving to present the unique, absorbing love stories that you enjoy most—books that are more than ordinary romance. Your suggestions and comments are always welcome. Please write to us at the address below.

Sincerely,

The Editors
Candlelight Romances
1 Dag Hammarskjold Plaza
New York, New York 10017

CHAPTER ONE

It was a perfect diamond in the sky, hanging above
the azure blue lake paused in flight. Resting now, it
seemed to be gathering momentum for some unknown destination. Brilliant reds and blues and
greens caught the crisp sunlight and scattered
across the June sky. And then, as if on cue, it puffed
out and swept up and away, moving like some
lovely mythological creature across the cloudless
expanse.

"Perfect!" Carly West's triumphant voice sang on
the breeze as she raced along the high bluff, her
multicolored skirt blowing in the wind. Thick black
hair flew from beneath a bright red visor cap and
her dark eyes flashed with excitement.

"What a beauty!" She expertly released more
string from the wooden spool and watched the silk

kite dip and curve, then soar back upward, the out-line of the bright white unicorn dancing majesti-cally on the wind.

Satisfied with her creation, Carly settled down onto the bank, the kite string secured in her hand, her cotton skirt bunched beneath her.

The bank was gray with dried brush and willows. Carly plucked one absentmindedly with her free hand and rubbed its soft fur against her flushed cheek. Her sandaled feet were braced against an intricately twisted tree root that jutted out from the side, protecting her from the fifty-foot drop to the thread of sandy beach below. There was a clearing in the brush here and she could see the stretch of coastline, at once smooth, then textured with the waves' deposit of millions of tiny fossils and stones.

A slight movement at the water's edge diverted her gaze. Through the thick undergrowth and knot-ted stumps she spotted a man in a gray suit—a suit? —his pants' legs rolled nearly to his knees. His bare, well-muscled legs gleamed bronze against the in-tense blue background of sea and sky. He was a tall, easy-moving man with a whipcord strong frame. Although he was too far away for Carly to distin-guish his features, there was something in his stance, the angle of his head, the playful way he reached out to pat the beautiful Irish setter frolick-ing at his heels, that she found immensely appeal-ing.

Carly watched with amusement as the dog

darted in and out of the waves, playing tag with the frothy whitecaps. "A Norman Rockwell painting come to life," she mused aloud, "though far more enticing."

A sudden tug at her hand brought her attention back to the virgin flight of Unicorn I. The wind had suddenly switched directions and the kite was sucked down, then swerved sharply inward. Carly leapt to her feet but was not in time to thwart its dive; in seconds the pristine unicorn was bound firmly to a dead branch protruding from the bluff about ten feet up from the beach. The knotted string was enough to put an Eagle Scout to shame and held the kite immobile against the scrubby cliff side.

"Damn!" Carly's brows drew together as she peered through the dense brush, then glared down at the kite. It was far too steep a drop for her to climb in sandals, and the nearest access path to the beach was nearly a mile north. She looked around for a possible remedy to her plight and her eyes lit almost immediately on the unsuspecting beachcomber and his dog, still strolling lazily down the beach.

"Hey!" Carly cupped her hands around her mouth and shouted. "Hey, mister—help! Up here—" But her voice traveled less than half a dozen feet before being blotted out by nature's forces.

Dropping the spool to the ground, she gathered

her skirt around her knees and ran like a March hare along the beach, shouting at the top of her voice. The man, blissfully unaware of his pursuer, paused now and then to skip the waves with flat stones, then moved on, the dog still romping at his heels.

Carly stopped in her tracks. It was futile. He'd never hear her. "Well, this is my last chance," she puffed, her breath coming now in jagged spurts. She whipped the red visor from her head and stared at it. For an instant she reluctantly fingered the cross-stitched words on the visor: *Affairs of the Air.* "Come on, hat, you're my last hope." She pushed apart the dense, tangled brush and, with a mighty swing, flung the hat down toward the man and his dog. Like a well-trained Frisbee, it skimmed smoothly through the air. Then, just before reaching its mark, a strong current of air picked it up and carried it out over the lake. The dog spotted it first and barked as if discovering a strange breed of bird flying out to sea. The stranger shaded his eyes with the flat of one hand and he, too, followed its surprising flight over the water.

As Carly was about to turn back in frustrated defeat, the wind switched directions and gently, purposefully, boomeranged the hat and gently deposited it at the man's feet.

"Hey down there . . . mister!" She waved her hand in wild circles above the bushy growth.

The stranger bent and picked the hat up off the

ground and carefully dusted off the sand. She could see him looking at it intently while the Irish setter sniffed with mild interest. Both man and dog, then, stood together and stared out at the endless stretch of water, as if expecting the magical appearance of a treasure ship or yet another gift from the sky.

"Oh, no," Carly moaned, then yelled again with what breath she had left. "No, not that way! Me . . . look at *me*—up here!"

The man scanned the beach, shading his eyes from the drifting sand. For a moment Carly thought he had spotted her. And then, as she stood alone at the top of the bluff, still flagging her arms above her head, she watched the man in the suit calmly shrug, place the red visor on the dog's auburn head, and continue down the beach.

"Damn, damn, double damn!" Carly's slim shoulders slumped. "First I lose my kite, and then my hat! What's next?"

The unicorn kite was nearly forgotten the next day as Carly found herself caught up in a sudden barrage of welcome customers spilling into her shop, Affairs of the Air.

Carly smiled patiently as a matronly woman on the other side of the counter fussed with her two young charges. It was an unusually warm day, and even with the constant breeze blowing in off the lake, the air lay heavy in the small kite store. One of its less desirable effects was that the hands of the small children touching the colorful kites were sticky.

"Guess I should get air conditioning in here," Carly said, shrugging apologetically to a plump woman pulling her wallet out of a too-full purse. Her words held little meaning, however, for Carly West was in no financial position to install air conditioning in Affairs of the Air.

She gave the woman her change, laughed politely when the elderly gentleman beside her commented for the third time on her T-shirt, which read *Go Fly a Kite* in lettering of every color of the rainbow.

The day had gone extremely well so far. Although not yet noon, the cash register had been ringing all morning. Bless the tourists, Carly thought. The Northwestern students would buy her out if they could, but she knew she needed the wealthier patrons from the North Shore suburbs and the inevitable tourists straying north from Chicago proper to give her any real security. And summer brought them out in droves. Now, if only she could come up with a sales plan for the more meager months in late fall and winter.

Maria LaSala, her full-time assistant, assured her something would happen this winter, that this was *the* year. She felt it deep down in her substantial Italian bones. Affairs of the Air would truly fly. Well, Carly thought, let's just hope Maria is psychic in addition to being indispensable!

Carly looked up with a start. It was the red visor in his hand she noticed first. Unmistakably hers. He was turned toward a giant poster outlining the dangers of Ben Franklin's kite experiment and she could only glimpse his strong profile from across the room. But she knew it was he. The Norman Rockwell painting with the terrific body. Holding her hat! Her relief at having her hat walk in was tinged with another emotion: annoyance. After all, he was responsible in a way for the torn and battered unicorn kite she had finally retrieved from the branches yesterday afternoon. The windy incident had proven costly; the expensive kite was beyond repair. True, *he* wasn't really aware of any of that. But he certainly could have been, had he been a bit more observant!

"Maria, would you please take over the cash register for a moment?" Carly called to the plump woman who emerged immediately from the back room, her shiny gray-black hair pulled tightly into a bun.

"I was just coming anyway, dear." Maria's strong low voice was thick with affection. Before the door swung shut behind her, Carly caught the spicy tang of garlic sauce and olive oil and knew Maria had been putting together one of her incredible pasta dishes for lunch.

"Um-m, smells terrific!" She flashed Maria a smile and slipped from behind the counter. Brushing her hair off her wet forehead, Carly approached the man who so boldly displayed her cap.

He was intently reading the poster now, oblivious to her presence behind him. At closer range her eyes were drawn to his broad shoulders, slim hips, and long firm legs. He was wearing a suit again today but the cuffs of the pants were rolled down. Then her eyes rose to the gray-flecked temples, the strong, commanding profile.

"It's about *time* you brought it back," she teased quietly, her soft voice daring him to turn around and face his accuser.

He did turn, slowly, and then she saw the smile that would dictate the flips and pulsings of her heart for days to come. Up close he was excitingly handsome, and Carly's instinctive reaction was to fantasize what fun it would be to get to know him. "So . . . it's the gray-suited beachcomber. A rare species."

"Excuse me?" He spoke in a deep husky voice as he met her gaze. Then his eyes scanned the words curving across her breasts on the thin T-shirt.

It doesn't take that long to read four words, mister, she grumbled silently, trying to banish the flush that spread quickly across her high cheekbones and on down her neck.

"Ah, you must work here." He seemed not to notice her reaction. Taking a step toward her, he held out his hand and caught hers in a solid grip. "I'm Matt Linton, and I have one question. This poster—" A frown formed as he pointed to the picture of Ben Franklin holding a kite, bright streaks of lightning zigzagging across the background. Beneath the picture was a set of rules for youngsters warning them about the dangers of duplicating Mr. Franklin's experiment. "He was a *hero*, a great inventor. Not a bad example—"

"Of course he was. But his experiment was actually very dangerous. Very risky."

"Sometimes it takes risks to accomplish great things."

"Granted." Carly met the blue eyes head on now, the hat forgotten. This was her turf, her topic. And sparring matches excited her. "But I'd prefer none of our youthful customers were fried—even in the cause of science. Twelve-year-old kids aren't always ready for such risks."

Matt Linton watched her closely while she spoke. He noticed the fiery glint in her eyes, and he liked it. "Agreed. But I hope Ben gets proper credit also."

"Absolutely! Who could not give Ben Franklin credit?" She drew him down the aisle to a long wall spanning the back of the store. It was painted white and covered from one end to the other with photos, diagrams, and posters of facts about kites and their history. "See?" She pointed to a pencil sketch in the center of a man floating on his back in a pond. He was propelled across the water by a kite looming ahead of him. And near it was another of the famous inventor with his kite flying high in a thunder cloud.

Beneath was a detailed description of his experiment.

"Bet you didn't know Ben Franklin used the kite to experiment with traction as well as electricity?" Her eyes danced with excitement.

Matt didn't answer but smiled slowly. Then his eyes widened as he scanned the expanse of information stretching across the wall. "This is quite a collection!" There were illustrations from Viennese manuscripts dating back to the fifteenth century detailing the construction of parchment kites. There were posters depicting scientific applications of the kite. There were photos of Indian festival kites and Korean kites and lovely hand-painted Japanese kites.

Matt let out a low whistle. "The owner sure knows a hell of a lot about kites. He must be a fascinating guy. Any chance he's around? I'd like to meet him."

"Yes and no."

Matt's eyebrows lifted quizzically.

"*Yes,* the owner knows plenty about kites. And *no,* she'll never be a fascinating guy. But you *can* meet her." Carly grinned and held out her hand in greeting. "Hello. I'm Carly West."

Her hand was immediately swallowed up in that of the older man with the piercing blue eyes. Her hand felt comfortable in his. "I'm glad you're enjoying my store."

"Your store." It wasn't really a question. He was

18

surprised and curiously pleased that it was her store. And it seemed right, somehow. He ran a hand through his thick dark hair, the slight specks of gray catching the sunlight that fell through the open windows. He looked at Carly again, as if reevaluating her in the light of this new information. She was young, he thought. But that was a purely relative concept, after all. Young to be owning a store. Younger than he. *A lot younger,* he thought with a certain curious interest. Her jet-black hair and flashing eyes sparkled in the clean sunlight and Matt Linton found his eyes traveling back to those eyes, then roaming over the soft curves of the gypsy-like woman's body. She was refreshing, he thought, like a gust of pure lake breeze that tantalized your senses and awakened you to beautiful things.

Her eyes had canvassed him also. They were focused on the hat in his hand.

"My hat! I'd almost forgotten. You're holding my hat."

Matt had forgotten also. Somehow forgotten entirely why he had entered this world of kites. He handed it to her immediately. "The hat, of course. I'm sorry—" There was a slight apology in his tone but it was mixed, Carly noticed, with amusement he seemed somehow determined to hide. He was actually shy! Carly suppressed a grin.

"This charming hat chased me down the beach yesterday, Miss West. It, ah, it was much too nice to throw back to the waves so I—"

"It chased you, Mr. Linton, because I threw it at you!" Carly's eyes flashed and carefully she related the saga of the kite.

Tilting her head back, Carly looked straight into his eyes. She noticed with a strange tingle of power that he shifted beneath her gaze, as aware of her presence as she was of his. "Well, kind sir, thank you for returning my hat." She plumped the visor back on her head where it nestled among the thick waves. "Now tell me, Mr. Linton—" Carly groped for another topic of conversation—one that would keep her at this wonderfully captivating man's side a little bit longer.

"Carly—" A woman's voice wound its way around the stacks of kites. "Could you help out at the register? There's a line forming."

Reluctantly, Carly pulled her eyes away from Matt's, thanked him again, and hurried back to the counter.

"How are we doing, Maria?" she asked, running a quick tally on the cash register. "Looks great!" She caught the older woman's quick glance and revised her statement. "Well, it looks better than yesterday."

They smiled easily at one another.

"That was one very sexy fella you were talking to. I did not recognize him—"

"Maria," Carly scolded, feigning total innocence. "I thought you hated gossip—"

"Gossip I hate. But a little *amore*—that's like good

vino. Sweetens the life." She winked mischievously and turned back to the waiting customers.

Carly welcomed the diversion. Welcomed the excuse to banish thoughts of Matt Linton from her mind. Their brief conversation had been charged with an undercurrent of intensity that excited yet unnerved her. He was oddly shy, reserved, but in a most tantalizing way! Carly West had not felt butterflies in her stomach since she was eight years old —yet somehow Matt Linton had unleashed a whole fleet of them!

Matt stood at the far corner of the room watching Carly. Her eyes sparkled as she talked to the customers and even across the distance he could sense the magic of her manner. She's like a gypsy, he thought. Free, alluring, her ebony hair a cloud of smoke about her high, finely carved cheekbones. As she worked, she lifted her hair unconsciously with one hand and let it fall around her shoulders. He knew he should leave. Should get back to his classes at the university. But he didn't want to go. His head was full of kites and fantasies and Affairs of the Air. And his senses were too highly strung. He didn't want to leave. He wanted to see more of Carly West.

Wandering closer to the counter, he pretended interest in a display of stunter kites and watched Carly out of the corner of his eye.

"Thank you and I hope your family enjoys these," Carly said to a departing customer. Then her eyes, fringed by those wonderfully dark lashes, opened wide in surprise. "Why, Mr. Linton, are you still here?" She looked at the kite he held in his hands. "Those stunter kites are wonderful! Perhaps you'd like to purchase one for your family?"

Matt looked in surprise at the kite. "My family?" He laughed. "Oh, no. You see, I'm a professor at Northwestern—visiting professor. I'm only here for the summer. I don't have a family here."

"A professor at Northwestern, how interesting. A lot of my students come from the university. What do you teach?"

"Aerodynamics." He smiled.

"Aerodynamics—perfect!" Carly stepped from behind the counter and took the kite from his hands. "This would be a perfect demonstration kite for you to use in your classes! Keep those kids awake on hot summer days."

"Well I don't know, I, ah—" Matt watched her in surprise as she held the kite up and pointed out its features.

"Really, it'd be great! I hadn't thought of it before, but kites are wonderful ways to teach certain aerodynamic principles. Besides that, they're beautiful and *everybody* loves a kite!" Carly reached into the bin and pulled out several more kites. In minutes she had them laid out on the counter and was explaining in great detail the obvious merits of kite demonstrations.

"Well, I don't usually present material that way—" Matt looked at the kites skeptically.

22

"Ah, come on, Professor! It would be marvelous! And young people learn better with hands-on experiences. Maybe you ought to take five or six?" Carly smiled and Matt followed the lift of her face, feeling his usual reserve melt faster than lightning.

Hands-on experience, he thought, his eyes following the gentle curves of her body. Yes, I suppose we all like that experience now and then. A sudden warmth shot through him. "Well, it is an interesting idea," he conceded hesitatingly.

Maria watched in amusement as Carly continued her spiel. She had no doubt in her mind that the man would leave with kites. And would *like* to leave with Carly!

"There are a few tricks to launching this kite, Professor." She looked up, her dark eyes wide and sparkling. "It's not that easy to fly. Be sure the center section of the spar is at fifteen degrees or—"

"But," Matt cut in, wondering how she had talked him into this crazy idea, "I don't know anything about kites. I'd need some assistance. I'd need—" At that moment an idea popped into Matt Linton's carefully ordered mind, an idea that surprised him as much as it did Carly and Maria when he blurted it out. "You'd have to come and demonstrate, or show me how to launch it. I would pay you, of course—"

"Now wait a minute, Professor—" Carly protested. Then her thoughts raced ahead and she began to map out a strategy. After all, this was a business proposition. With a little careful forethought, there might be a way to milk some publicity out of this. Besides, doing business with Matt Linton might have other advantages too. . . .

"Well, actually, Professor, I'm going to be test flying some new kites tomorrow. If you're free, I could teach you some basics and we could talk further then. Are you interested?" Her fingertips rubbed slowly over the smooth cash register keys.

"Well now, yes. I think I could manage that. After all, I don't want my investment to be a flop." His eyes flashed with sudden unspoken meaning. "When and where?"

"The bluff where you absconded with my hat. Around noon. I'll bring lunch."

"Terrific. I'll be there." Matt gathered up his pile of kites, which had magically multiplied to twenty-five, handed Carly a check, and lingered a moment longer. Again, he didn't want to leave.

"Is there anything else I can help you with?" she asked, noting his hesitation.

Matt's eyes sparked with energy. Oh, yes there is, Carly West. There certainly is. . . . "Ah, no." He smiled again at the gypsy woman stopping the breath in his broad chest. "Not right now." And balancing twenty-five kites in his arms, Matt Linton edged slowly through the door.

CHAPTER TWO

Standing on the sun-bleached steps of the Student Center, Professor Matt Linton looked like an unlikely candidate for a picnic, and he knew it.

His suit was unbearably hot and as wrinkled as an elephant's hide by the soaring humidity. His lean, sweat-drenched body yearned for the feel of thin white slacks and a T-shirt, the rise and fall of a polished deck between him and the sea. No ocean here. No matter what the natives said or how loudly they said it, Lake Michigan was *not* the ocean. He thought of Stanford, of the ocean, of his small house by the sea. Salt! That's what he missed. The sharp sting of salt spray on his face and chest.

With the back of one hand he wiped the salty beads of his own sweat from his brow. Narrowing his sky-blue eyes, he squinted against the sunlight's white glare at his watch. "Damn! Twelve-thirty already!" No time now to change. Wouldn't you know that sleeper in the third row would pick today to wake up and wax eloquently on lift and drag! Maybe he should suggest a nap to some of his other students.

Shifting his leather briefcase to his other hand, Matt yanked off his tie and stuffed it into his pocket. The one thing he was *not* about to do, heat or no heat, suit or no suit, was miss lunch with that gypsy-like woman from the kite store. . . . Carly West. His mind played over her name just as it had been savoring her image all night, and all morning until Mr. Crockett awoke in class with his questions. Carly West. At the thought of her, the pleasant tightness in his chest returned. It was an interesting, almost forgotten sensation. A smile played across his lips, traveled to his eyes. But it was hidden there beneath the dark sunglasses Matt slipped on as he headed across the campus lawn.

A few students glanced up as he passed, fewer waved. The lawn, which sloped away in the direction of the lake, was dotted with blankets, young people, and radios. The few scattered benches were filled. Even the trees had students in them. They were busy with the all-encompassing ritual of college life that classes such as Dr. Linton's unfortunately interrupted. Male and female, in large groups and alone, the kids were "doing their own thing." Matt smiled, thinking of his own student days. Too long ago, he thought ruefully. Back when a maryjane was still a little girl's strapped shoe.

Matt's rented Datsun was an oven, but as he sped north along the winding Lake Shore Drive, the lake breeze swept through his hair and washed away the morning's heat. He topped the rise overlooking the beach and parked.

Carly was there waiting for him. He saw her at once, down a short winding path near the bluff. She wore a shining white blouse, a gaily patterned skirt, and her hair was a smoky cloud around her face. She was beautiful. As cool and fresh and bright as a day lily, its face tilted toward the sun. He could have watched her all afternoon. The sight of her refreshed him, and made him forget the heat.

When Carly spotted him she waved and began to pull a glimmering ribbon of color down from the sky.

"Well, hi. I had about given up on you, Professor Linton!"

"Sorry. I had a roomful of Einsteins this morning, each wanting to voice his own theory on friction, form, and induced drag." Matt walked almost to her side and stopped. His smile warmed her face. "I see you went ahead with the maiden voyage without me."

"Ah, time waits for no man—at least not when the wind is right!" Her laughter stirred the air the way no breeze could. His eyes trailed to the source of the delightful sound. Her teeth flashed white behind curving rose-petal lips. Her throat was cream rising from the milk white of her blouse. The pale hollow at the base of her throat trembled as she spoke.

"Matt, you look terribly uncomfortable. Would you rather make it another time?"

"What? Oh, the suit! I really had intended to change. I almost *never* fly kites in a suit—"

Their rich laughter mingled on the wind.

Carly turned halfway to look at him from behind the dark fringe of her lashes. She felt very brazen, yet very much at ease.

"Well, Professor, are you ready for some *practical* aerodynamics?" She quickly, expertly rewound the kite string, drawing the previously forgotten kite from the sky.

"Wait! Why pull it down? Can't I just fly it?"

"Professor! Would you suggest sending an astronaut into orbit and letting him sleep through lift-off? Oh, no! Besides, the work here *is* the pleasure!"

Something flickered behind his eyes as he stared at this dark-haired gypsy of a girl. "I agree, Ms. West. One hundred and fifty percent. Here, give me that beauty—"

Carly handed him the spool and the kite. Matt ran his fingers carefully over the silken, flawless surface, tested the arc and the tension of the frame. A sudden recklessness overtook him and he savored it hungrily.

"Tension is perfect," he said, his voice molded with insinuations. "Beautiful!"

"Yes, I am proud of her. She's modeled after an ancient Persian kite. Did the silk screen myself. See"—her fingers reached across his to lightly trace the pattern—"this motif was found on the temple walls dating back—Ah! There I go," she laughed softly, clasping her hands behind her. "You mustn't get me started."

"No, please go on. I'm fascinated."

"I'm sure!" Lifting her chin, she looked at him with her dark, laughing eyes. "Go on. Go fly a kite!" She stepped back.

But before he could begin to play out the line, she'd reached for the spool again. "Nope. Won't work. First you've got to take off your jacket."

He shrugged it off and dropped it on her waggling fingers.

"Okay. Now the sleeves. Up!"

Chuckling, Matt unbuttoned the cuffs of his blue oxford shirt and rolled them up over his muscular forearms. "Satisfied?" he asked with glinting blue eyes.

"Just trying to be helpful," she countered. Like heck! came the unbidden protest of her conscience. You really wanted to see what was hiding beneath that jacket. What are you doing, girl!

Matt saw the color rise above the pristine white of her blouse. It flattered him, flustered him. His fingers burned when Carly placed the kite spool back in his hand.

"Okay. Here I go. Do I need to give it a running start?"

"Just a bit. All you need to do is let it find the breeze. She'll fly for you!"

Matt ran off along the bluff, one arm jutting up behind him, the other curved in front playing out the string. He was all angles and movement. Smooth fluid play of muscles and bone. Intense concentration.

Carly felt a sharp tug at her stomach. As if the kite string had somehow gotten itself wound around her. Why was this stranger with the shining blue eyes having this unnerving effect on her equilibrium?

The kite bumped along behind Matt's loping frame, refusing to become airborne. It sent crowds of crickets into flight, blew clouds of dandelion fluff in his wake, and left a faint trail through the tall grasses.

Matt cast a laughing "What do I do now?" glance over his shoulder, only to see the woman's rich brown eyes sparkling, her mouth tipped up in a grin. His dark brows leapt. "Can't get the damn thing up!"

Carly hooted, the laughter springing from her throat. "I've heard that can be quite a problem. Listen . . ." She had to stop and catch her breath. "Don't work so hard!"

Matt discovered he couldn't run, laugh, and launch a kite at the same time. He opted for laughter. "Thanks! Just what I need. A critic! And with a bawdy sense of humor, no less!"

"Come here. I'll help," Carly said, feigning contrition. Her eyes gave her away.

Matt chuckled and brought the kite back.

Carly placed her hand lightly over his, reached up to grasp the kite's tail, and began to run. Matt matched her pace, shortening the length of his stride to fit hers. He was acutely aware of the graze of her legs against his, the brush of her shoulder against his chest. Her heavy dark hair blew against his throat. Her scent filled his senses.

Carly's shout startled him. Looking up, as she was, he saw the kite lifting into the sky, drawn heavenward by invisible hands. "Hey, that's great! We did it!"

Stepping back, Carly relinquished the kite to Matt's control. "You're lucky! The wind's picking up!" It blew her skirt against the slender outline of her hips and legs and tossed her dark hair into her face. She caught the thick tresses in one hand and held them at the nape of her neck, out of her eyes. Those dark eyes were riveted to Matt's face, to the open pleasure lighting his handsome features. Something almost boyish played across his face as he watched the kite, squinting up into the bright summer sunshine. She could see the fine crinkling of lines at the corners of his eyes and mouth. And how full his brows were . . . not bushy, but definite, lighter than his hair, and without the peppery sprinkling of gray. His hair at his temples and neck had tightened into rough curls. Carly felt a sudden tingling at her fingertips, an urge to wind one damp strand around her fingers, or touch the smooth plane of his cheek. Instead she nibbled vaguely at her lower lip, narrowed her eyes, and measured the uneven pulse of her blood.

Then Matt's brow furrowed; his smile vanished. The kite had begun to buck and sway and was most decidedly earthbound.

Carly moved close behind him and wrapped her arms around his waist, setting her hands over his. With the ease born of long practice, she tautened the string, shifted the angle of the spool, and guided his fingertips to a better grip. "There. Now you'll be fine. Just relax."

"You *must* be kidding!" A sexy laugh emphasized his words. Emphasized the feel of his ribs pressed against the soft flesh of her inner arms. The supple play of the muscles across his broad back pressed against her breasts.

She cocked her head at one angle and looked at him.

He caught her eyes and held them, his smile deepening into a dimple at the right-hand corner of his mouth. "Ms. West, I'm better than fine, right now."

"Not a very serious student, are you, Professor? What kind of example is that to set for your pupils?"

"Luckily I don't see a pupil within five miles—" His glance warmed her face, *"Very* lucky, in fact," he said, his voice dropping to a husky pitch.

Carly loosened her hands and stepped back, shivering slightly. The tone had changed; the effects of Matt's teasing were no longer playful fun. Now when he spoke, Carly felt her control ebb away, felt a flutter in her chest that made it *very* difficult to think about kites.

"Ah, Professor," she edged away, welcoming the coolness of distance. "You've been hiding things from me. You're just a natural kite flyer. Admit it."

Matt grinned at her over his shoulder. "Thought you'd never notice!"

"Really, Matt. Tell me about yourself. I don't know anything about you."

Matt hesitated. He looked from Carly up to the kite in the sapphire blue sky, then back to Carly. "I'm a very one-directional guy. Can't walk and chew gum at the same time. May we bring the kite down?"

"No sooner said than done!" And it was true. Retrieving the kite from its perfect landing, Carly asked, "How about lunch? Can you eat and talk—if no walking is involved?" Her eyes teased and excited him.

"I'll give it the old college try." Matt hunkered down beside her on the grass, as close as he dared to his slim, enticing companion. He watched her as she unpacked the picnic basket, enjoying the quick sure movements of her hands and the slant of her shoulders beneath the thin white blouse. He liked her habit of tossing back her hair and smiling. She was free, spontaneous, irresistible. . . .

"Look, Professor!" She interrupted his thoughts. "Antipasto—prosciutto, provolone, fresh melon—" Carly's eyes were black and as opaque as coal as she popped a round salty olive into her mouth. *"Mamma mia!"*

Matt eyed the repast with hungry awe. "You're a gourmet!"

"Me? Of course not! I can hardly boil water." Carly laughed lightly as she drew a bottle of Chianti out of the basket. "It's Maria, my assistant. She's wonderful. If it had been left to me, we'd be eating my area of expertise—"

"Kites?"

"No," she giggled. "Sandwiches. Anything that can go between two pieces of bread. Peanut butter and banana, ham and Swiss, liverwurst and pimento—"

"Stop! Enough. A toast to Maria!" Matt uncorked the wine and poured the rich, ruby liquid into two clear plastic cups. "Cheers."

"Salut! Now," Carly said with an impish smile, "back to our ground rules. Will you tell me something about yourself?"

"Such as . . . ?"

34

"Well, have you always taught at Stanford?"

Matt seemed to hesitate, then he shook his head, his eyes holding hers. "No. I spent some long, not very happy years at NASA, running stress tests on experimental craft."

Carly gasped, her eyes shining, "But that should have been so exciting . . ."

"It was exciting. But not happy," he answered cryptically, his tone precluding further comment. "I *have* enjoyed Stanford; it's a very interesting place to teach."

"And how long is Stanford going to have to survive without you, Professor Linton?"

"Just for the summer. I'm back on the schedule for the fall semester."

"Ah, I see." Carly nodded, swirling the wine slowly in her cup.

Just as well, she thought, staring into her cup of wine. That limited the possibilities nicely. There was something a little too appealing about those sky-blue eyes.

Matt, unaware of her thoughts, experienced a sudden, sharp twinge of regret. He could see the end of the summer telescoping toward him. Fast. Too fast. Yet wasn't it just yesterday he was thinking how nice it would be to be going back home?

"I'll be here for all of July and August," he added eagerly.

"Oh." Her voice was soft and noncommittal, her

eyes wide and clear of emotion as she looked at him. "Are you enjoying yourself here?"

"More and more each moment."

Carly's lips tipped upward in a smile.

"What else do you want to know?" he asked softly. Her questions would reveal as much about her as his answers would about him.

"Well, what do you miss about California?"

Ah, a subtle woman. He narrowed his eyes against the bright sun and thought aloud. "The sea. The redwood desk in my office where my knees fit just right and my elbow has rubbed a smooth hollow and where my favorite coffee cup is still waiting. And my children are there. Close by though I don't see them much. My daughter, Tracy, is just starting law school, and David—well, he's twenty-five and trying to find himself, as the kids say—" Matt leaned forward, wrapping his arms around his knees, his glance steady on her face. He read the question in her dark eyes. "I'm divorced," he said. "Ten years."

A sudden smile played across Carly's lips. "Have an olive, Professor." Plucking one from the paper plate, she offered it to him.

He took it from her, but it remained forgotten in his hand; he was too busy watching her.

And she was watching him. The sun lifted warm highlights from his thick wavy hair and his eyes glinted at her from beneath his brows. Blue eyes, shining on her with a powerfully sensual light.

Then, with a shake of her dark hair and a deep

breath, she reminded herself of why they were there. She and the visiting professor. The kites. She was a businesswoman. And this was a business lunch.

"Professor—" The word came out in a lurch. Carly cleared her throat and began again. "Professor, I've got a proposition for you—" She waved away the smile of surprise that flashed across his lips. "A *business* proposition. I've a very mercenary heart which I hide behind this cool exterior."

"I bet!" Matt laughed.

"Gospel. And I've got you to thank for this idea. You see, if *you* can use twenty-five kites in *your* class —a number that makes a pleasant, profitable dent in my inventory—then why couldn't other instructors do the same? Just think, kites in comparative cultures classes, in art history, demonstrating ancient patterns and designs; in science classes, a prime example of one of nature's most elemental forces—"

"Carly West, *you* are a prime example of one of nature's most elemental forces—the wind and the sky, fire and air, all—"

Carly blushed and hushed him. "Eat your lunch, sir. For a professor, you certainly are a romantic!"

"Am I?" His eyes darkened. No one had ever described him that way before. His frequent forays in those bleak years past had smacked heartily of sex—without an ounce of romance. His gaze turned outward again and he jumped; Carly was staring at him. He couldn't read the thoughts behind those dark eyes but he felt the intensity of their gaze.

Matt chuckled self-consciously. "Why the deep dark look, Carly?"

"No reason. You . . . you seemed to drift away for a minute there, far, far away—"

"Years, not miles," he replied.

"Oh." What else could she say? She didn't know this man but she felt drawn to him, perhaps because she sensed he was so different from her. He was a total stranger, and unless her business proposition could also serve as an excuse to see him again he was likely to remain one. A little shiver ran up her spine. The thought already carried a burden. She pushed it back into the recesses of her mind and smiled. "Matt?"

"You've got all my attention now, Ms. West," Matt answered with his warm grin. "What else do you want to know?"

"Well, if it's not getting too personal . . ." Carly's voice trailed off suggestively as she leaned far forward, her hair spilling like ink over her shoulders, brushing her breasts and his chest as she curved toward him. "Tell me—do you like mustard on your provolone?"

Surprised laughter rumbled in Matt's chest. "Why, you are a wicked woman, aren't you, Gypsy?" His hands wound around her body. One settled on the small of her back, wrinkling the smooth white blouse as he pulled her to him. His other hand snaked into her hair, his fingers tightening in the smoke-dark cloud. And then he kissed her.

Carly felt the warmth of his breath on her lips just a heartbeat before the firm, cool surface of his mouth found hers. It was a sweet, lingering kiss. Matt brushed his lips across hers, matching their shape to his own, savoring their pliant, yielding texture. He nuzzled the corner of her mouth, exploring it with the probing tip of his tongue as if some secret might be sprung there.

He groaned softly in delight when Carly's tongue slipped silkily between parted lips to touch his.

Using his elbows and hips to brace them, Matt held her to him and lowered her down on the grass.

Carly imagined she could feel each blade of grass bending and yielding beneath her weight. One blade after another, they folded their sun-warmed lengths and bent earthward to provide a cushiony bed for them both. The warm loamy scent of the heated earth rose about them. Crickets hopped to safer ground and resumed their droning song. One lazy fly buzzed across the picnic basket, landed on Matt's shoulder, and flew away.

Carly was sure this was heaven—or at least St. Peter's Gate. Her hands trailed exploringly across his sweat-dampened back and down over the hard curve of his buttocks. She felt his loins press and arch against her, stirring embers to flame deep within her. A swift, potent response blazed into life and she dug her fingertips into his flesh.

Matt groaned and drew his hands gently down the straining rise of her breasts. The intimacy of his touch shocked Carly back to her senses. "No . . . no, Matt—" She tore her lips away. "I . . . I didn't mean—"

"Didn't mean what? I did." His voice was low and filled with desire. "I meant to kiss you, Carly West. And I'd like to do it again."

A thin sheen of moisture coated Carly's forehead and she felt it as well beneath the thin layer of her clothes. "Matt, please. I really did want to talk business with you. I didn't mean to let this get out of hand." Her voice quavered slightly and Matt read the caution in her tone. He edged back a bit and ran his finger down the side of her cheek. Then, letting his hand drop to the grass, he sat back and watched her face.

"Matt, I *did* plan this as a business lunch. I . . . I'm not sure how we strayed so far from that, but—" Her shoulders rose and fell in a quick shrug. "Kite flying does crazy things to people, me included. But now we had better get back to business."

"Why?" He grinned.

"Because it's important to me. Really."

"All right. Then I'll be serious. Your idea is interesting, Carly. But I'm not sure if Northwestern is the place to launch it. Perhaps some Scout groups, or—"

"Matt Linton! Wait a minute here. I'm not talking about flying paper airplanes! Do you have any idea what role kites have played in history? How *old* kites are? Why, kites date back to the very beginnings of human civilization! They are important in the most ancient legends and folk tales! They . . ."

The lecture went on and on and Matt felt himself settling back and enjoying it, relishing the flavor of it—*and* Carly West—and actually learning from her convincing stream of facts and figures and stories about kites.

It wasn't long before Carly detected the change in his eyes from skeptic to believer and she jumped at the chance to seal the agreement. "So it's a deal then?" Her voice wound down to a soft, convincing query.

Matt fingered a lock of her black shining hair, then watched it settle back against the whiteness of her blouse. "I . . . I guess I could talk to a few of my colleagues. Now, they might not agree, mind you, but I'll try. I'll see if I can set up some appointments for you. But you'll have to give the pitch yourself—"

Carly's thoughts were racing ahead. This could be such a boon for Affairs of the Air. Such wonderful advertising. Maybe just the thing she needed to get her business out of the red. "That sounds perfect, Matt. When could you do it? When could I do my demonstration? Tomorrow?" Her eyes were bright with excitement.

41

"Sure," he said impulsively.

"Can you arrange it that fast?"

"Of course." Somehow he would, only because he didn't want to let this sky gypsy get away from him.

"That's great. Thank you. And don't forget to invite people from the comparative cultures department and art history and—"

Matt's laughter rumbled over the tall grasses and on out over the water. He held her gaze; behind them the wind and waves tangled together, then murmured softly against the shore.

CHAPTER THREE

The next morning things were once again back into perspective: the kite lectures at Northwestern loomed on the horizon, a bright and hopeful business deal, and Matt Linton—well, he was far beyond that horizon. One of those utterly delightful, utterly impossible things that blew in and out of her life like a Lake Michigan breeze. A visiting professor from Stanford, here for a summer teaching the N.U. masses. Then gone again. What did it matter if sky-blue, gone-straight-to-heaven blue eyes had thoroughly disturbed her sleep last night? What did it matter if she could close her eyes and vividly picture him standing at the water's edge, its blue motion lapping at his sturdy legs beneath the rolled-up slacks? What did it matter? She'd easily banish him from her desires, like Godiva chocolates and Dom Perignon champagne—just another luxury she couldn't possibly afford.

Carly laughed aloud to the near-empty store and slapped the counter, sending a pile of papers scuttling across the oak counter top. She scooped them up, piled them neatly beneath the counter, and reached for her keys. Three o'clock. A half hour to get to Northwestern and knock the socks off the esteemed faculty. She grinned, ready, and headed for the door.

"She's a real businesswoman, gentlemen. I think you'll all be suitably impressed." Matt slid down into the lounge chair and listened with half an ear to the conversation that followed.

Well, he'd done his part. Now it was up to Carly. How had he ever let her talk him into this crazy idea? All he could remember from the business portion of their conversation was the lilt to her voice, the refreshing laughter that escaped her lips, and the wonderful way the sun painted streaks across her thick, silky hair. He checked his watch and fidgeted in the chair.

It was nearly three-thirty. Where in the hell was she? She should be here by now. He'd gone out on a limb for her, and Matt Linton didn't spend much time out on limbs. He was nervous.

"There's still a few minutes, Linton." Jake Harrison, chairman of the Art History Department, had watched Matt's restlessness grow from the tapping-table stage to unabashed concern within the short

44

span of ten minutes. "We're a patient group, Matt, you'll see."

Laughter followed. The four department heads were willing to wait. They were more than a little curious to meet Matt Linton's "kite lady," whom he claimed had unusual business acumen, innate intelligence, and an incredible knowledge of kites. Matt had sung her praises at length.

Wondering what was keeping Carly, he rose and drifted away from the department chatter. Concentration had been hard fought all day long. Vivid images of the gypsy kite flyer followed him, dusting his thoughts as he moved from class to class. Flashes of the raven-haired woman scattered his aerodynamics lectures into tiny, separated pieces. He felt distracted, loose in the limbs, fragmented. The flu, he thought. That must be it. I'm getting the summer flu. But Matt Linton knew all along he was drastically misdiagnosing his condition.

He wandered over to the neat row of narrow, second-story windows and glanced down at the casual campus life below.

His heart reacted first—a quick skip and surge of heat. Then incredulity, dismay, and uncontrollable desire took over. Matt pushed open the casement window to get closer.

The campus square was a colorful checkerboard from above. A lazy movement of shapes and hues winding across the green spaces. But in one section of the near-pastoral setting the movement was quicker, more alive, nearly frenetic. Carly had arrived.

She wore a watery-sleek scarlet jump suit that flowed over her gentle curves with grace and subtle sensuality. The thick mass of ebony waves was absent today, pulled up and tucked beneath a shiny black aviator's helmet. And like the Pied Piper of Hamlin, she glided smoothly across campus, one hand raised as it deftly guided a magnificent black and white box kite along cushions of air, attracting an array of followers.

Heads turned; bodies stopped; people stared. But mostly students fell in step beside and behind her, lured by the sparkling smile of the woman in red and the airborne shape that splashed ever-changing shadows across their pathways as it passed through the sun's beam.

Matt Linton's breath caught in his throat as he followed her movements. A wave of humid heat circled his body and he felt dizzy, out of touch with reality. He moved away from the window and the air cleared.

When he looked back, she was still there, still a crimson flash, still attached to the kite, still the focal point of every person on the campus! Matt groaned.

Slowly he turned back toward the group of professors. "Gentlemen, Ms. West has arrived."

Before the men could respond, excited laughter and raised voices drew Matt's attention back beyond the window.

Carly, ever the teacher, had wound the kite line around a small boy's eager hand and ran with him now along the grassy earth. The vision of the slender woman in crimson and the square, youthful figure leading the giant kite had created its own rapt audience of students, professors, and passersby. Buoyed by the spirit of the crowd, the child suddenly wrested himself from Carly's grasp and ran pell-mell across the square, the kite a streak of silver and black chasing behind him. His eyes, fastened on the kite, shone with delight and his short legs rotated in a whirling staccatoed rhythm.

The warning erupted from Carly's lips only an instant before the collision. The child slid to a stop at the wide base of the FM radio tower and soulful eyes raised to the tangle of strings wound tightly around the symmetrical rungs midway up the structure. And slightly above that, bobbing lightly against the sun's silvery glare, was Carly's kite.

From their second-story vantage point, four department heads from the School of Arts and Sciences watched in utter fascination. The fifth was already out the door and on his way to witness Carly's caper at closer range—and deter it, if possible, from running a disastrous course.

A crowd had gathered near the tower and Matt worked his way through it quickly, his mind struggling with fear of what he knew Carly would do next.

And she did. Taking a quick moment to wrap the

child in a friendly, reassuring hug, she wiped the frightened tears from his eyes. Then, without a backward glance, she pulled her sleek body up to the tower's first slat and continued heavenward like a spider up a silken web. Bystanders shielded their eyes against the sun's blinding glare and cheered her on, the lovely helmeted kite flyer, her molded body a crimson streak against the azure sky.

"Good grief!" Matt muttered as he watched her slender hips rotate up the ladder.

"Say, Linton, quite a lovely tush she has, your staid, serious kite lady—" Jake Harrison pulled up beside Matt and slapped him jovially on the shoulder, his squinting eyes filled with amusement.

Matt threw him a silencing look and moved closer to the base of the tower. It was too late to stop her and it would be foolish to pursue her. So Matt stood helpless and watched as she climbed halfway up the eighty-foot tower and swiftly unwound the cord from the tower. Securing it around her own hand, she glanced down, nearly ready for the descent. Matt's look caught her and stilled her for a brief moment.

"Hi, Matt," she called. "Sorry I'm late!"

With a final tug she released the kite and shimmied quickly down the tall signal tower. Matt's arms lifted with sure instinct as she neared the bottom. Carly released her hold and fell full into his body. Strong arms slid over the crimson cloth and wrapped firmly against her chest.

"Dammit, Carly. You could have killed yourself," he growled against her cheek. "And please take that bowling ball off your head!"

Laughing, Carly ignored his words and relished the liquid warmth Matt Linton's hold sent floating through her limbs and circling down deep inside her. At last the ground firmed beneath her feet and she steadied herself, then eased slowly out of his embrace. With one swift movement she pulled the helmet away and freed the tangled black waves that fell to her shoulders and framed her flushed cheeks. The solid smoothness of Matt Linton's chest and gentle pressure of his hands against her back and shoulders lingered in Carly's consciousness.

Finally, issuing Matt a brilliant grin, she stepped apart and said, "I do believe we have a business appointment, Professor Linton. Would you care to lead the way?"

Later, in the air-conditioned coolness of the faculty lounge, Carly charmed them all, just as Matt knew she would. They even managed to see beyond her "uniform" as she called it—the incredible scarlet jump suit with *Affairs of the Air* curving across the front—and listened intently to her dissertation on the history of kites as related to the arts and sciences.

All the department heads agreed that Carly's series of lectures and demonstrations would be a wonderful asset to the summer program. Some, particularly those whose classes were held in the older campus buildings without air conditioning, were especially vociferous in their approval. They knew without a doubt that the soporific atmosphere that set in when the lake breeze died and the humid, heavy air pressed down upon them would be shattered forever by Carly West and her kites.

When the meeting ended and the professors headed back to offices or homes, Matt and Carly lingered in the darkening shadows.

"Matt—" The corners of Carly's mouth quirked upward in a wry grin. "Come on. There's a little bar I know of just off campus. I'll buy you a beer."

"God knows I *need* one!"

"Was the afternoon too much for you, Professor?" Carly teased.

"Not the afternoon. Or the morning. Or yesterday. *You.*"

Carly's heart somersaulted into her throat. Why did the man have to be so honest, and so enticing? Steadying her voice, she said, "I hope I didn't overdo it—the drama, I mean. I wanted to be sure they'd remember me."

Matt's deep eyes were twinkling when they caught hers. "I'd bet my tenure on it! Judging from the looks on their faces, I think they'd sooner forget their own names. As a matter of fact . . ." He took a step closer and brushed a loose strand of midnight dark hair from her cheek. "I think I've forgotten mine. Would you say it once for me?"

The electricity of his touch sent her pulse racing. "Matt Linton," she whispered.

"Just a little louder."

"Why?" she laughed, stepping back to open a space between them. He *should* have been speechless with her charm and wit; instead *she* was the one having trouble with words.

Matt's voice was coaxing. "Because I want to hear the sound of my name on your lips, and—"

"Professor—" Carly narrowed her gypsy eyes, a warning Matt would later learn to heed. "If you wanted things repeated, you should have brought a tape recorder."

"Oh, you're fresh!"

"No, thirsty. Parched to the very soles of my feet. So, if you're still interested in that beer . . . ?"

"That's not all I'm interested in." He paused and Carly could almost see him reassembling his cool, staid facade. "But that will do for now."

The bar was a wonderful hole-in-the-wall rathskeller with sawdust on the floor, patches on the dark leather of the booths, the air conditioner puffing on high, and a TV blaring noisily above the bar. When they stepped into the dim interior, Laverne and Shirley were cavorting across the tiny screen.

"There's an empty booth—" Matt took hold of Carly's arm, guiding her toward the back of the room. Beneath his fingers he felt the slide of the slick, polished fabric and the warm firmness of the flesh it sheathed. How he wanted to touch her! It

51

was like a physical hunger, this desire she caused in him. If her elbow could do this to him, what about the touch of her thigh, or the silken valley between her breasts? Matt dropped his hand, letting his fingertips trail slowly down her arm to her wrist.

As his touch released her, Carly slid into the far side of the booth.

"Come here often?" Matt asked.

"Only after a particularly harrowing day." She smiled, dark lashes eclipsing one eye in a sexy wink.

"It's fascinating. It looks like a movie set." He scanned the room, then propped both elbows on the table and leaned across to Carly. "Can't you just hear the director? 'Okay, fellas, build me a beer joint. Make it dark and noisy, filled with kids,' and everyone who has ever been young and had a beer on a college campus will nod and say, 'Yup, I was there!'" Matt smiled. "Funny, isn't it, how we perpetuate our own myths?"

"And what myth are you perpetuating, Professor Linton?" Carly had her chin resting on her cupped hands, and her eyes were dark, bottomless pools watching him.

Matt frowned. "None." He shook his head. "Trying hard not to."

"I don't believe it." Tilting her head to one side, she teased him. "What lurks beneath that serious, scholarly exterior? A spy perhaps?" She chuckled at her own joke and shook her head. "Male stripper? That's why I see you only in the daytime"—she

measured his six-foot-plus frame with her eyes—
"right?"

That brought the laughter rumbling to his chest.
"Sorry to disappoint you, lady, but beneath this
scholarly, serious exterior lurks a serious, scholarly
type. Dull. Sorry."

"Don't be!" The words were out before she could
stop them. Luckily the shadows hid her blush. "I
mean, I think you're perfect . . . for . . . for a
professor, I mean . . ." Oh, Carly West, just be
quiet! she commanded silently. Her cheeks were
scarlet.

Matt watched her with laughing eyes. "Don't
stop now. I'm just beginning to enjoy this conversation."

"Conversation ended, Professor! We need a few
beers."

"Bartender—" Matt promptly signaled across the
noisy room. "Two drafts."

Carly took a sip as soon as the tall, chilled glass
was set on the table. She loved the feel of the cool
foam on her lips. "Ummm. Good and cold. Thank
you."

"You're welcome. And you've got a mustache! It's
very attractive."

Carly laughed and swiped at her lips with a pink
tongue. "Funny how this brings back memories.
When I was a little girl my father always let me have
the first sip of his beer."

"Sounds like a nice guy. Does he live here in town, your father?"

"He's dead. He died eight years ago, just a few months after my mother. Which is also funny, considering that they hadn't lived together, or spoken to each other, for five years. One of life's small ironies."

"I'm sorry."

"Me, too. I miss them both, though they were far from ideal parents. I'm mostly sorry they didn't make each other happy while they had a chance. But marriage seems to have a way of ruining things . . ." Carly shrugged and looked up to find Matt staring at her with disconcerting intensity. "Did I . . . What is it, Matt?"

"Nothing."

She heard the canned TV laughter in the silence between them. Matt ran his fingers through his hair and glanced away, then back to Carly. His handsome features softened. "It's nothing. I was just thinking how difficult it is to live up to other people's expectations."

"Meaning what, Professor Linton?"

Matt blinked and shook his head. "No, I wasn't meaning you, Carly. It was just a philosophical observation. Allowable from us serious, scholarly types." He flashed a crooked, boyish smile that melted her heart and brought the heat rushing back to her cheeks again.

Carly tilted her head back and gave him a long,

thoughtful look. "Matt, I have a feeling there is more to you than meets the eye—"

"What?" Reaching across the table, he brushed his fingers lightly across the back of her hand, traced the ridges and valleys of her knuckles in sensuous slowness, then entwined his fingers with hers. "What exactly do you mean, Carly West?"

"I'm not quite sure. Call it intuition—"

Matt tightened his hold. "Call it fear?"

Her eyebrows shot up. "Fear? Oh, Matt, you don't know me very well at all." She tried to bite back a grin, but it trembled on her lips, then spilled over her face, making dimples in her cheeks and fire in her dark eyes.

Matt threw her a confused look. "I didn't think it was that funny."

"Well, you serious, stuffy types," she said jokingly.

"Who said anything about stuffy?" He crossed his arms over his chest and glowered at her from beneath his dark brows.

Touchy, touchy, Carly thought. Must have hit a nerve. Perhaps he does see himself as stuffy; the typical professor with pipe and patches on the elbows of his jackets. But with those eyes? That incredible body? Unbelievable. No, there was another man beneath the professor's facade, Carly suspected. And the thought of discovering and liberating him filled her with delicious anticipation!

A mixture of mischief and remorse flavored her

voice. "Perhaps the wrong choice of words, Professor. How would *you* describe yourself?"

Matt uncrossed his arms and leaned toward her, his mouth curved in a secret smile.

Carly's eyes widened in surprise. When he touched her again, she felt the mischief drain through her toes, leaving a quaking hollow in its place. She flicked the tip of her tongue over suddenly dry lips. Had he read her thoughts? He had!

Matt's smile broadened and Carly felt a stab of purely sexual awareness that pierced right through the thin fabric of her jump suit. She shoved a smile into place and lifted one shoulder with a casual shrug. It was definitely time to regain control of this situation. "Well, Professor? Perhaps I ought to read some of your secrets."

"Maybe after a pizza. I'm starving. Besides, there are no secrets."

Carly smiled and took one of his strong hands in hers. "Well, let me see here," she ran a finger along the intricate fan of lines in his palm. "Ah, I see a very persistent, heartless man! And here I thought all professors were kindly gentlemen with perfect manners."

"Sorry to disappoint you." Matt smiled slowly, his discomfort quickly melting beneath her touch. "What else, gypsy?"

His eyes were narrowed now, holding her, and she felt the flickers of arousal circle her again. The ground was less firm and she shuddered, dropping his hand. "You're right. We need food! I'm too hungry to concentrate on your Life Line right now," she said shakily.

"What's the matter, Carly? Why are you suddenly so nervous?" His hand snapped up and closed around her wrist.

She didn't want him to know what a powerful effect he had on her. Never had she felt so tantalized, so excited, so close to the edge—of what? She felt caught at the thought and held it tightly, like a weight pulling her back to earth. It was all impossible. Crazy!

"This is crazy," she whispered.

"I know. What I don't know is what to do about it."

Carly counted to ten, ten breaths of cold, real air. "Shall we try a pizza?"

"Reluctantly. Most reluctantly."

They polished off the pizza in relative silence, ordered another beer, and caught a glimpse of the Fonz plying his adolescent charm on a weak-kneed cheerleader. The news blared to dozens of disinterested patrons, until a shot of the campus itself filled the screen. There was the college common, Carly's kite wound around the radio tower, and Carly herself, perched forty feet off the ground on the tower scaffolding, her clinging scarlet jump suit revealing her every lovely curve.

"Oh, Matt. Look! That's me—"

"God, I don't believe it."

"Hush. Let's listen."

When the thirty-second spot ended, Carly sat dazed, her hands pressed to her flushed cheeks. "Oh, Linton . . ." she groaned.

"It's okay, Carly. I know it's embarrassing—"

"Embarrassing?" Carly blinked twice, then burst into laughter. "No, oh, no. I wasn't embarrassed. Just frustrated that I didn't know they were taping. I'd have turned around and shown off my chest."

"You would have what?"

"My T-shirt, I mean, Professor," she repeated, chortling, and she lightly pulled the jump suit open to reveal a colorful printed T-shirt. "See?" she asked pointing at the store's name emblazoned across her shirt. "I could have had some free advertising. Do you have any idea what a thirty-second TV spot goes for these days?"

Matt shook his head. His husky laughter mingled with hers. Never had he met anyone so unpredictable. So tantalizing. Watch it, fella—you're in trouble and the countdown's not even begun. Steady. But the flash of her smile, her whimsy, her blithe spirit beguiled him.

He was staring at her, only half listening to what she was saying, when a chair scraped at his side.

"Hey, mind if I join you? That was you on TV, wasn't it? Pretty neat kite you had there."

"Yes, well, thanks." Carly smiled at the intruder. "And who are you?"

"Oh, name's Wyatt. Jeff Wyatt. I'm really into

58

lighter-than-air machines, but kites knock me out, too. That was a beauty. A Conyne, wasn't it?"

"Why, yes!" Carly replied, her surprise and admiration clear in the lilt of her voice.

Matt interrupted, his own voice flat. "I thought you called it a military kite, Carly." He didn't really give a damn about kites at the moment, but he was determined to distract Carly from this garrulous, overly friendly young man.

Carly waved away his comment. "I did, but its technical name is Conyne. It was patented by an American inventor, Silas Conyne, in 1902 and, well . . . not many people know that." She turned her attention back to young Wyatt. "You should come to my shop sometime and let me show you . . ."

It went on like that for hours, or so it seemed to Matt. He ordered another beer for himself and downed it in a hurry. Then he sat watching the two young people, feeling like the intruder himself.

Anger burned in his chest. Irrational. Foolish. He knew all that. But he couldn't help himself. He glared into his empty glass, drummed his fingers on the table. It gnawed at him, nonetheless, until he put a name to it. He was jealous. Jealous as hell.

The thud of the heavy beer mug hitting the table jarred the conversation and Matt felt a perverse pleasure at the look of surprise on their faces. "It's late. I've got to get going." He slid from the booth like a man whose seat was on fire. "Coming, Carly? Or would you prefer to stay?"

"No, I'm coming," Carly answered breezily. "Nice talking to you, Jeff. 'Bye."

The warm humid air wrapped Matt in an oppressive embrace as they stepped from the bar.

Carly tossed her hair. "Goodness, it's as thick as soup out here. We'll have a storm off Lake Michigan by midnight for sure."

"Oh, you predict the weather as well?"

"Oops." Carly stopped dead in her tracks. "Was that sarcasm I heard in your voice?"

"No. Sorry." His words were sharp as pistol shots. "Forget it."

Carly shoved her hands into her pockets and tilted her chin until the lovely oval of her face was raised to his. "What's the matter, Professor?"

"Nothing."

Her coal-dark eyes searched his and Matt shifted in discomfort. "You didn't have to come away," he added gruffly. "You were having fun and you looked like you belonged there with that kid Jeff. Hell, you're a kid yourself."

"I am not." She slipped one hand out of her pocket and tucked it into the crook of his arm. "I'm thirty. Besides which, I *wanted* to leave with you."

"Hmph," he growled, but something new had come into his eyes. Where the anger had been, something else was smoldering.

"Hmph, yourself, Professor. Now let's run before the storm catches us."

CHAPTER FOUR

Carly West's eyes danced and the moisture that had collected in her palms was now a badge of triumph as the students' applause rang in her ears.

"Thank you, Professor Shane! It was a delight being here."

"Listen, Ms. West," the pleased sixty-ish professor beamed, "it was *our* pleasure entirely. Why, you had us flying high!"

The plump, gray-haired man laughed enthusiastically at his own humor, his eyes crinkling into tiny slits. "You gave those young folks enough material and, ah . . . va-voom! today to keep them awake through several classes. Perhaps the whole summer."

And indeed she had, Carly admitted to herself as she walked down the nearly deserted hall a short time later. They had soaked up her lecture like sponges. They had explored and probed and hungrily digested the history of kites in different cultures from the mystical element in Japan to the wonderful Egyptian kite-flying legends. Carly felt a strange thrill, an unanticipated high.

I wonder if it's this same thrill that brought Matt to a college campus, she mused. This opportunity to add a dimension to the lives of the kids, to share the thrill of their discoveries; I wonder if *that's* what lured him away from the limelight life of NASA.

Carly glanced down at her watch, then took an unplanned sharp right turn and quickened her pace. Matt would be finished teaching soon. Suddenly she needed to see him for just a moment. Not just to thank him, but because he was the one person she really wanted to see. She couldn't explain it, but there was something about him that attracted her the way a breeze attracted a kite.

At the end of the hall Carly paused and collected herself. Room 203. That was his door. She pushed it open a crack and a sheath of darkness spilled out. Carly impulsively slid into the dark room. Down on the raised platform in the tiered lecture room a bright screen was filled with flickering images. From somewhere near it, tucked away in the dark shadows, Matt's deep voice lent life to the slides that changed with the steady click-click of the projector.

She couldn't see him, but the rich timbre of his

voice painted images as vivid as lightning across a blackened summer sky. She slipped unnoticed into an empty chair and was effortlessly drawn into the magical images of space being flashed across the screen slowly.

"This last shot was from the space craft as it circled the earth," Matt's voice explained. "It was a clear, black night. Imagine for a moment being drawn to that window, peering out into the darkness, perhaps with one arm circling someone special. Together you scan the universe. Then he—or she—leans over and whispers softly into your ear, 'There certainly is a beautiful earth out tonight—' "

Light laughter and the sounds of bodies shifting in chairs drifted over the rows of seats as the lights flicked on. "You see what's ahead, ladies and gentlemen? We haven't begun to explore the romantic elements of space travel. That's for *your* generation!"

"Ah, Professor Linton," a young woman with a noticeable Southern accent drawled from the first row, "no generation has a monopoly on that. Now if you're looking for a research assistant, why I'd be most happy to—"

Laughter muted her sentence and circled about the room. The class was used to friendly teasing and casual flirtations; more than one female student had given in to secret fantasies of being "alone" with the charming "older" man teaching her aerodynamics class. Matt handled it with his restrained charm, and continued his lecture.

Carly listened to him, enchanted. She watched his eyes sparkle with excited pleasure as the students peppered the air with questions. As he talked, he walked slowly back and forth across the front of the room, moving with easy grace, his hands slicing the air as he made a point or shoved comfortably into the pockets of his oat-colored slacks.

There was a sensuous dignity about Matt Linton that drew Carly forward in her chair. The way he moved, his tall lean body, so perfectly proportioned, the strong, handsome face carved to a sensitive maturity. She tried briefly to imagine him as a NASA executive, caught up in the frenetic glamor of the public's dream to conquer space. There was an incongruity in the image that tugged at her, but as Matt turned toward her in response to a student's question she again caught the glint of the unknown in the magical depths of those blue eyes.

Carly felt a sudden twist of longing so abrupt she straightened in her chair with a lurch. Matt saw her then, her soft eyes and face flushed with unconscious desire, and his own eyes fastened on her with a firm hold.

"So the lift and drug elements—ah . . . rather, *drag* elements—" Matt stumbled over his words as several students followed the arrowed line of his stare and caught Carly's blush. But so delighted, and flustered, was he to see the raven-haired woman that he gave it no mind. Taken by surprise, he flashed a bright, crooked smile. Then, with Herculean effort, he twisted his mind back to his lecture and fought his way through the charged air long enough to bring the class to a fitting close.

"Okay. That's it for today. Read the next chapter for tomorrow. See you then—" His eyes swung automatically back to the woman sitting still in the last row of seats.

Long, smooth strides brought him almost immediately to her side as the room emptied about them. "What are you doing here, Ms. West, besides driving me crazy?"

Carly had kept her eyes on him as he raced up the steep narrow steps in his eager approach. Now he stood inches away and the air stopped moving between them.

"Well, actually, Professor, I'm here to evaluate this class." She feigned her most serious tone, drawing her brows together. "Perhaps you'd care to explain these new principles you're expounding. This 'lift and drug'—"

"Quite simple, ma'am." Matt leaned over and his hands stretched around her waist and curved slightly, applying gentle, pleasing pressure just beneath her rib cage. "I *lift*"—with one quick movement he brought Carly's body into sensitive contact with his own—"and then I *drug* the damsel out!"

Laughter bubbled from Carly as Matt swept her like a feather across the hardwood floor.

"Okay, okay, esteemed Professor! Your explanation receives an A-plus rating! Now, listen to me, you crazy educator type—" She eased herself gently out of his hold. "This is serious. I came here on official business. To thank you for convincing your cohorts that I *do* have some sense. And to invite you for dinner as a token of my appreciation." The invitation was out before the thought had fully formed in her own mind.

"Spoken like a true con artist . . . when I know what you *really* want is to ravish my body." Matt stepped closer and wound his fingers lightly through the silken waves of her hair.

Carly felt the heat rise between them and her head spun. He had taken her by surprise, throwing her totally off balance. It was not a situation Carly West was used to finding herself in; for once the tables had been turned.

Struggling to regain the advantage, she insisted, "Now be serious, Professor. *Dinner.* I want to take you to dinner. Really, I loved doing the kite lecture. It was fun, and even if it doesn't boost my business, it was worth it. And . . . I owe it all to you."

Matt grinned. "And I love being owed." His voice softened, and his eyes were warm on her face. "By the way, I knew you'd be great. Now, about this dinner invitation . . . ?"

"Saturday night all right?"

Matt nodded, an expectant smile curving his lips.

"What's your favorite treat, sir?"

As Matt opened his mouth to speak, Carly caught the glint in his eye and parried quickly, "Wait, I'm talking about food, Matt! You must have had an aphrodisiac for lunch!"

His mouth slipped back into an easy smile. "It's the lift and drug lecture. Does it to me every time!"

"*Food*, Professor."

"Yes, of course. Fish! I love fish, Carly—fresh fish—"

"Fish—" Carly began gathering up her notes. "That's great. I know the perfect place." And then, as quickly as one of her kites caught on a crosscurrent, she headed for the door.

Matt tried to stop her. "Carly, where? When? Don't run off so quickly."

"I have to." Carly threw him a softly carefree smile. "I've a shop to tend. I'll pick you up Saturday at six o'clock. Be ready! Oh . . . and the dress is casual—*ciao.*" And she was gone, the swish of her skirt melting in with the sounds of muted laughter and whizzing Frisbees from beyond the open window.

The raspy putt-putt of the shiny motorcycle was the only discordant sound on the tree-lined street. Streetlights were lit against the early signs of dusk, and the houses, tucked far back from the street behind great private hedges, were only to be guessed at.

Carly was late. Matt would probably tease her;

that is, if the motorcycle didn't leave him speechless. She breathed a tiny sigh and shook her helmeted head. You probably should have warned him, Carly West. Oh, heck. Surprises add spice to life. Surely Matt Linton wouldn't be averse to that. Her eyes flashed with excitement and her stomach took a pleasant leap at the thought of the professor waiting ahead.

Five miles up the road, Matt Linton was trying to keep a steady hold on his growing excitement. He ran a hand through his hair, then slipped his hands back into the pockets of his khaki slacks and paced through the low-ceilinged rooms of his rented carriage house one more time, his Irish setter close at his heels. The big dog barked and mouthed at Matt's hand, restless with unspent energy. "Know just how you feel, boy!" Matt commiserated with his pet.

At six on the dot Matt stepped out the front door. He couldn't sit still. Locking the dog in the kennel, he closed the gate behind him and walked down the long drive to the street. No sign of a car. Shoving his hands in his pockets, he leaned against a lamppost and watched the flickering shadows play on the sidewalk at his feet. He could feel the pounding of his heart beneath the tensed cage of his ribs. His face wore an inward-turning smile of anticipation.

A raucous caterwauling broke the stillness and raced up the street toward him. Yanking his hands from his pockets, Matt leapt backward and stopped, staring open-mouthed ahead. "Oh, no . . . I should have known . . ." he sputtered.

"Surprised, Professor? Hop on!" Carly held out a metallic blue helmet and patted the back seat. "Well, come on. The fish are waiting!"

"I'm afraid to think about *that,* Carly West. Something tells me they're not going to be filleted and almondined when I first see them!"

A wide grin lit Carly's face. Her eyes danced as they held his.

"Oh, no . . ." he whispered again. Then, with surprising ease, he straddled the rear seat, edging forward until his opened thighs formed a vise around her lower body, his feet braced on the frame.

Carly's grin slid off her lips like honey. Every shift of his body, every movement as he molded his body to hers, telegraphed along her nerves. The inside of his thighs pressed along her jeans-clad flanks. Her buttocks were snuggled within the cradle of his pelvis. If he moved again . . .

And he did, leaning forward until his chest coated her back. "Co-pilot to pilot—ready when you are!"

"Blast off . . ." Carly croaked, her throat gone dry.

"What's the matter?" The voice over her shoulder was warm with concern; the flicker of arousal and amusement in his blue eyes went unseen.

"N . . . nothing at all."

With the absolute minimum of movement possible, Carly gunned the cycle into life. They sped down Lake Shore Drive, their bodies meshed so tightly they cast a single shadow on the pavement.

"Hey, this is a great idea, Carly!" Matt called over the wind's rush. "Fantastic idea. I used to do a little hot-dogging back in my NASA days. I'd forgotten how much fun it was—"

"Yeah . . ." Carly muttered. She was having trouble keeping her mind on the road ahead. Every jounce and bounce brought them into electrifying contact.

Oh lordy, why hadn't she brought the truck? Or asked Matt to drive? A sharp turn brought a tightening pressure from his thighs. Could he feel the flooding heat of her body? What was he thinking?

Matt rode loose and easy behind her, grinning like a fox.

Their destination lay twenty miles inland, a small cabin on the shore of a glacier-carved lake. The cycle wound its way past the suburbs and onto the familiar country roads heading west, covered now with a soft blanket of dusk.

As they rode, the fevered pangs of Carly's arousal subsided into a rich warmth inside of her. Matt's grin softened into a smile of pure pleasure.

"Doing okay?" she called back.

"Better than okay," he answered, delighting in the way the soft smoky ends of her hair poked out from beneath her helmet to tickle his cheek and throat. "Where are we going?"

"To my very favorite place. It's called West of the Lake. My father's old fishing cabin. We're almost there."

The cycle sped down a thicket-lined dirt road and soon pulled to a spot near the wooden porch of a small, rustic cabin. Matt flung out his legs to steady them.

"What a beautiful spot, Carly." He spoke softly, hushed by the surrounding stillness.

Carly watched him pull off the helmet, liking the way his rough curls lay mussed and tangled against his head, liking the bronzed glow of his wind-burned skin. Suddenly she was just so happy to have him here. With her. Just the two of them. She hesitated to put her feelings into words but they spilled out.

"I'm glad you're here!"

The smile Matt returned was rich in emotion. Then he swung from the cycle and walked a little way into the woods.

Carly kept sight of him as he moved through the trees. His figure was lost among the myriad of shadows laced across the rough ground. "Hey," he called. "I found blueberries! At least I *think* they're blueberries. They're blue—"

"That's a good sign, Professor," Carly chuckled, moving up the wooden steps toward the cabin. "You can be in charge of dessert. But now we've got work to do. Come on. Stop shirking your responsibilities!"

Carly was gathering the fishing rods, tackle boxes, and a pair of battered, fly-decorated fishing hats when Matt made it back to the cabin door. He pushed it open and stood for a moment, framed in the doorway.

In that instant the outline of his body, the angles and curves and planes of his form, were engraved on her mind and she knew that whenever she closed her eyes, she would see him there, exactly as he was now, whether she wanted to or not.

As his eyes adjusted to the room's dim light, he saw her. "Exactly what I was afraid of," he said dryly.

"Me?"

"No. Not you, woman. The dinner plans!" He eyed the fishing poles and, laughing, pulled her into his arms. "Give me a kiss, if you expect me to catch my dinner."

"Is this blackmail?" Laughing deep in her throat, she felt the shocking rush of her blood like a river of surprise throughout her body. She ran her hands up his back and across the muscled span of his shoulders.

"Call it what you want."

Carly had one second to make her escape. She was too late. Slowly, surely, Matt lowered his face to hers.

His kiss was brief and fierce. He rasped his tongue across her lips, then pressed his parted lips against hers. Carly's breath caught in her throat as she felt his tongue press deeply, then circle her lips until she felt like her mouth was a ring of fire. This man was dangerous. He could steal her breath—and her heart—away, and he knew it. But was she frightened . . . or glad?

Weak-kneed, she wriggled from his embrace and gulped a soothing deep breath of air. "If we're going to eat, we've got to fish first. Come on!"

"Business before pleasure again, my darling Ms. West?"

"Definitely!" Chasing the quiver from her voice, she commanded, "Now gather that gear and we'll take the small row boat out."

"Aye, aye, sir." He snapped her a smart salute and followed her out the door.

They caught enough fish to last for days, *weeks,* Matt thought, considering that his appetite hungered for something with silken dark skin rather than scales. And he felt his longing grow with every chance touch and glance as they made their way through the dimly lit thickets and climbed the wide porch with their catch in hand. But he held himself in check. Behaved like the perfect gentleman. Bided his time.

Unnerved by the sexual tension that filled the small cabin, Carly stayed at arm's length while they fried the fish, set the table, and poured the wine.

They sat in silence at the dinner table, the night pressing down upon them beyond the wide open windows.

At last Carly broke the silence. "Pickle?"

"With fish?"

"It's wonderful."

"Sure."

Carly paused between bites and plucked a long spear from the pickle jar. She held it out to Matt but he shrugged in mock helplessness, both hands firmly attached to a hot buttered ear of corn.

"Oh, all right," she laughed nervously. She held the pickle up to his lips and he crunched a huge biteful halfway to her fingertips.

Carly straightened, every muscle in her arm frozen, her fingertips giving out frantic SOS signals.

Matt's grin was teasing, knowing. His eyes had darkened to the color of dusk. He edged closer and, watching her face, took another bite of pickle. This time her fingertips felt the graze of his lips and forced her breath high and shallow in her throat. She knew what she wanted to do. Drop what remained of the pickle, tangle her fingers in his hair, and touch his lips with her own. Instead she sat there, mesmerized by his touch.

He placed a tiny kiss on her fingertips. "You were right."

"Always." Carly somehow found her voice.

They both laughed.

"Remember that."

"Oh, are you stockpiling ammunition?"

"I get the feeling with you that I just may need it." Carly tossed her hair back and lifted one bare

74

shoulder in an attempt to push the wayward strands back behind her ear.

Matt watched her, fascinated. Never had a woman's most casual movements bewitched him so. The simple shrug of a bare shoulder awoke the fire in his loins.

Don't look at me that way, Matt Linton, Carly begged silently. What do you see? What do you want?

Carly dabbed a napkin to her throat, then fanned it desperately in front of her face. "Whew. It has gotten hot again. Not supposed to happen in this part of the country." She nervously began to gather the odds and ends of their dinner, aware of Matt's gaze never leaving her, aware of the tender and amused glint in his eye following her every gesture.

"Whew . . . hot. Don't you agree?"

"One hundred percent!" He pulled his upper lip down over a wide grin.

Carly narrowed her eyes and stuck out her chin. "Oh, *you* are not hot, I take it?"

"Oh, I am!" he laughed, a deep resonant laugh that brought a wild somersaulting feeling to her stomach.

"Well, I for one intend to do something about it."

"And so do I, darlin'!" Matt matched his words with a quick backward thrust of his chair, and he was standing there in front of her, his hands on her arms, lifting her to him. Lifting her until she stood facing him, their bodies matched length to length.

Carly looked up, trying to find the right words. The sensible words. But already his mouth was lowering to hers. "Matt, I . . ."

He kissed away the rest of her words. His lips pressed against hers, searching to fit hers exactly, exploring the yielding surface of her mouth with barely restrained passion.

A tiny moan died in Carly's throat. Her arms flew up and wound about his neck. Standing on tiptoe, she pressed against him, her breasts crushed against the wall of his chest, her hips locked within the curved bow of his, her thighs touching his. Pure sexual awareness flamed at every point of contact; it was as though she were sheathed in a translucent flame of sensation. Never had she known a man like Matt before. Never had she felt this way before.

With sudden daring, she parted her lips and slipped her tongue across his, tasting the firm, sweet moisture of his mouth.

Matt groaned. His tongue darted out to circle hers and lead it hungrily back into his mouth. She ran her tongue across his teeth, delved the corners of his mouth. Coolness and heat were mingled there, promise and desire.

His arms tightening around her waist, Matt lifted her higher against him. His hands moved slowly down over the small of her back, circling in slow sensuousness until he cupped her buttocks and held her passionately against the hardness of his arousal.

Carly drew away slightly, caught the fullness of his lower lips between her teeth and nipped.

"Oh, Carly . . ." Matt groaned against her mouth. His breath was warm and sweet, melting her like butter.

"Yes, Professor?" she purred, her head falling back.

"I think something's burning . . . and it's not the fish!"

With a wicked grin, she slid her hands up to his chest and folded her arms in the space between them. She leaned back into his embrace. "I've got just the thing!"

"Uh-oh. I think I'm in trouble. Gypsy, you look like you're plotting something—"

"Something perfectly innocent. Something to cool us off. A swim!"

"What?"

"Come on. The lake is delightful. You'll love it!"

"Oh, no I won't. You're not getting *me* in that fish-infested water!"

Her throat filled with laughter, Carly broke away and dashed out onto the porch. She kicked off her sandals and ran lightly down to the water's edge.

Matt followed reluctantly, his hands shoved deep into his pockets. "I don't think I want to do this—" He stopped a good three feet away from the water and eyed her warily. "How do you get me into these kinds of situations?"

"It's good for you, Professor. Loosen you up. Come on!"

He shrugged, indicating his clothes. "Even if I wanted to, I don't think my alligator here swims."

"That's easy to solve. Take your clothes off. I won't peek." She winked and stepped into the shadows.

Matt heard the rustle and silken slide of clothes and underwear, and then a splash as Carly slid into the water. He saw the serpentine flash of one bare arm and a halo of droplets in the first shimmer of moonlight as she swam into sight.

The water was chest high, just barely hiding the curve of her breasts when she stood, though her nipples were hidden beneath the opaque surface of the water. Her hair was spilled ink, a darkness deeper than the night sky behind her. She smiled, teeth flashing between parted lips, and lifted one hand to wave.

Matt thought he was going to die. Felt his soul lift from his body and sail over the moonlit water to her, to this woman with the magic spell. And he knew he would never be whole again until he had her.

Standing there in the cool, pale moonlight, he shed his clothes.

Carly watched. And he knew it. He was glad for the firmness of his body, the hardness of his stomach, the width of his shoulders, the leanness of his flanks. Smiling softly, he stepped into the water and swam to her.

They circled each other slowly, then Carly's arms were on his shoulders. His hands found her waist and they kissed again. Their lips were wet and the water dripped from their hair down over brows and cheeks. Again Carly felt that wild leap of her heart and wondered fleetingly if it would blot out consciousness, so overwhelming was the sensation. Suddenly she was totally aware of her nakedness, there so close to him, the wet vulnerability of her body. When his hands again moved downward, she let her body drift against his, burying her face against his shoulder.

He held her close, murmuring her name into her dark, wet hair.

"Yes, Matt. Yes . . ." she breathed, answering the unspoken desire in his voice.

She felt his arms curve around her body, beneath her thighs, behind her back. The pebbly lake floor dropped from below the soles of her feet, and she was in his arms, suspended there in the moving darkness of the water, caught between its coolness and the undeniable heat of his body. He gathered her close, and she felt the pound of his heart, heard the harsh catch of his breath in his throat.

Carly stroked her fingertips over the flexed muscles of his upper arm and across his wet gleaming chest. Groaning, Matt kissed her eyelids and the curve of her cheek. She brushed his wet hair back from his brow, and traced a droplet of water down his cheek to his lips. He kissed her on the mouth, lightly at first, and then with ever-deepening passion. Their breaths merged and became one as his mouth slanted across hers, devouring, burning, urging her to a fiery response. Carly felt reality spinning away. Her world narrowed to the delicious urgency of his kisses, and she was swept away on the violent current of his desire.

He began to move, and Carly caught her breath as she felt the familiar buoyancy of the water fall away, and she was held only by his arms, and the magic of this moment. A flooding pleasure swept through her. Half closing her eyes, she saw the gleam of moonlight on his naked flesh, the same golden moonlight that rippled along the surface of the lake.

Matt hugged her close and strode toward shore, cutting through the water, letting it slide from their fevered bodies. The wide ripples slid to his waist, then his hips, then his thighs. He looked like a Greek god stepping from the ocean's depths and Carly trembled, wanting him so badly.

He carried her in to the one comfortable bed and laid her on the quilt. He stood there for a moment, his eyes devouring her, drinking her beauty, touching her everywhere with wonder and delight. "How beautiful you are, my gypsy."

Carly flamed beneath the heat of his gaze. "No . . . no, I'm not," she giggled, one hand fluttering self-consciously across her breasts. "No, my ribs stick out—"

"I love your ribs."

She laughed. "No . . . and . . . and I've got this tiny birthmark here under my breast—"

"Beauty mark! Stamp of approval from the gods themselves." She felt the close, rough brush of his hair as he bent and kissed her lightly beneath her breast. "Any other points of contention?" he whispered against her flesh.

"Matt, you are crazy!" she laughed in delight.

"And you are beautiful! And I'm going to make beautiful love to you. Right now, if you'll say yes." A glint of amusement flickered through the desire in his blazing eyes. "And if you say no, I'll probably die; explode into a thousand pieces right here before your eyes!"

"Then I'd better say yes, Matt. Yes . . ."

Matt leaned down to kiss her salty wet lips, murmuring soft love words against them. His hands wandered over her lovingly, in pure delight, stroking her thighs, drawing delicious patterns of fire on her stomach. Her ripe breasts, rose-tipped and tantalizing, trembled beneath his touch.

Abandoning herself to the rush of heat in her body, Carly rolled onto her stomach, reached low, and touched him, her small slim hand sliding deliberately over his nakedness.

Matt moaned, the pleasure so sharp and unexpected it flashed up his loins and across his chest. He couldn't breathe.

"Oh, Carly!" he gasped. Drawing the breath slowly back into his lungs, he whispered, "Lordy, you've got my toes curled."

"How nice." Her answering laugh held a fierce quickening of arousal. "It's the least I can do, Matt Linton."

"No . . . no," he laughed with total delight. "Far . . . from the least! Not the most, I admit—" The tight muscles of his stomach jumped with his laughter, then the laughter became a moan as her hand stroked him steadily. "Oh, Carly . . ."

"Do you know how beautiful *you* are, Professor?" she whispered. "An absolute wonder. An engineering marvel."

"Carly, I can't stand it. Come here, come here to me." He reached down to her on the bed, but in her nakedness she slipped away, rocking back on her heels, her hand still touching him. "Carly . . ." he growled, uttering a sound of mingled pain and pleasure. It was more than he could stand. Leaping into the bed, Matt shoved her playfully onto her back, then straddled her, one knee on either side of her slim, enticing hips. He bent and kissed her, his mouth hot and demanding. Carly answered his kiss with a startling fierceness of her own. Her tongue curled about his in insatiable desire, and her lips felt swollen and love-bruised. Their kisses began and ended and began again without a pause for breath.

She could have wept when he pulled his mouth away, but it was only for an instant, for the flicker of time it took for his hands to mold around her hips and swing her weight up on top of him.

His sky-blue eyes held her dark shining gaze, adoring her, wanting her. "Yes?" he whispered.

"Yes! Oh, yes, my dearest . . ."

And his hands tightened on her hips and he drew her down, down on top of him. She felt the velvet thrust of him within her, the touch that is the most intimate of all touches, and, arching back into his hands, she let him fill her completely.

It was like the final burst of rockets on the Fourth of July.

Carly felt her life explode within her; his life exploded and mixed with hers. It was a wild flight through blazing skies, high above the spinning earth. Two heavenly bodies soaring in a vacuum; nothing existed for each but the other.

When she could think again, breathe again, she held him tight, hands curved like petals around the smooth curve of his buttocks, wanting the moment to last forever. She lay quietly in his arms, her cheek against his, his breath warm on her face, and thought about this man . . . this surprising, somewhat bewildering, wonderful man! This man whose touch, whose smile, whose every word had come to mean so much . . . so quickly. This man she knew she was beginning to love.

For a second a sharp fear leapt to her throat and

she wanted to cry out. What had they done? What had they begun?

She opened her dark brimming eyes and looked at him, only to find him already studying her with such tenderness and caring that her doubts dissolved like so much smoke on a night breeze.

"Hello, Gypsy," he whispered, stroking her gently from shoulder to hip, his fingers moving so slowly, as if to memorize each curve and line, as if to reassure himself that she was real . . . and *here*, warm in his arms.

"Hello, Professor," she whispered back, nuzzling her head beneath his chin so that she could rest her cheek on the warm solid curve of his shoulder. "Happy?"

"Lord . . . yes!" he answered fiercely, pulling himself away an inch or two to look at her. "And you?" There was just the slightest edge to his voice, a hoarseness that betrayed him. He had caught that flicker of panic in Carly's eye when she had first stirred; his heart was aching with it now.

"I'm very happy, Matt."

"Are you sure?"

"*Yes*, I'm sure," she laughed, pushing her fingers contentedly through the rough hair on his chest. She stopped, cocked her head, and stared at him intently. "What's the matter?"

"Nothing. I just thought . . ." He swallowed around the sudden tightness in his throat. "When

84

you first opened your eyes, there was something
. . ."

He let the words trail off into silence, but there
was a deep worry line etched between his brows.

Gently Carly rubbed her fingers across the harsh
lines of his frown, soothing it away. "That was nothing, Matt. A moment's worry, a thought—"

"Damn!" He grabbed her wrists, trapping her
hands against the heaving wall of his chest. His
breath exploded in a curse. "Damn, I knew it! It's
the age difference, isn't it? You were thinking I'm
old enough to be your father—*not* your lover!"

Carly gasped, then laughed in astonishment and
disbelief. "That's not at all what I was thinking! My
father? You would have had to have been making
love at age ten—"

"Eleven," he growled.

She laughed. "Well, close to the Guinness Book of
World Records!" Tangling her fingers in his thick,
wet hair, she drew his face back roughly until she
could see into his darkened eyes. "That, Matt Linton, is not at all what I was thinking. Old? Oh, no—
not old," she continued in a voice husky with desire.
"Not *this* face." She gently touched his eyelids and
the rough planes of his cheeks. "Not *these* shoulders." She ran her hands over their muscular width.

Matt trembled. His anger and confusion kindled
into hot passion. Her hands were on his body and his
body flamed. "Carly, Carly . . ." he breathed into
the dark spill of her hair.

And suddenly, for them both, these light teasing touches became too much to bear. All their former passion reawakened, sliding over their bare, misty bodies like warm sweet honey.

Carly rested both hands on his chest, her heart racing wildly, her lips parted and moist. "I thought you were tough as nails, possessed of an unshakable calm?"

Matt drew her closer and closer, until she was stretched out on top of him, a slender, delicate weight balanced on his broader frame. "I thought so too, Gypsy. What are you doing to me?"

Her answer was in her eyes and her touch. When she brushed her palms against his furry chest, his nipples hardened at her touch. The rough mat of his hair flattened and tickled beneath her palm.

"You're all salt and peppery here too." She smiled softly.

"Is that good?" he whispered, watching her with adoration in his blue eyes.

"Very good. My favorite seasoning." She bent and pressed her lips where her hands had been. His skin was warm, and from it rose the musky scent of his arousal, a heady blend of familiarity and strangeness. She flicked her tongue over first one nipple and then the other.

Matt's breath caught in his throat, then hissed free like steam escaping from a furnace at the boil.

Laughing softly to herself, drunk with pleasure, Carly tipped her head back and looked up into

Matt's face. His eyes were hazed, the pupils gone wide and dark. He looked down at her, his face raw with emotion. "Carly, I am slowly losing my unshakable calm."

"If I said I'm sorry, I'd be lying. You are the sexiest man I've ever met."

"Carly." The rough timbre of his voice was charged with arousal and anticipation. "You, my sky gypsy, are the most beautiful woman in the world."

Folding his arms around her, he rolled over, pulling her beneath him. His kiss seared her mouth, quickly fanning the smoldering embers of their desire into bright, fierce flame.

And they made love again, and then slept in each other's arms as the stars wheeled silently overhead toward dawn.

CHAPTER FIVE

The days slipped by on a soft cushion of delight as Carly West and Matt Linton embedded themselves in one another's lives. Carly felt herself filled with delicious glee, as if she were tottering on the brink of something enormous and never before imagined.

Together they snatched time away from teaching and selling kites and drove to the country where they wandered down goldenrod-bordered dirt roads side by side; they drank cider from farmers' cold buckets and slipped down on cool, damp earth beneath the dark lines of gnarled old trees and explored lovingly the fine lines of each other's dreams and wishes.

Surely every person, Carly thought as they moved into the thick of summer, is owed one joyously gorgeous summer in her life. A time unconnected to any other, without consequences, recriminations, responsibilities. And surely this time was to be hers.

Yet, as she busied herself with the burgeoning sales preceding the Fourth of July celebrations, a gnawing, uncomfortable feeling began to build within her; she was becoming very attached to Matt Linton. And that hadn't been in the plan. Carly concentrated on her tiny store filled to the rafters with kite buyers and tried to shake off the uneasiness.

"Beth," she yelled over the constant buzz of customers, "would you please help Maria drag out another box of red, white, and blue kites? They're selling like hotcakes!" Carly brushed her forehead with the back of her hand and watched her blond friend dash after Maria into the back room. She'd cajoled Beth into taking a sick day from her office to join the organized chaos as they all worked frantically to fill the orders and help dozens of tiny bodies choose just the right kind of kite.

Carly watched the bright upturned faces of three small children standing nearby. How excitedly they eyed the shining colors and fondled each kite. They understood the wonder, and a little bit of each one's soul would soar skyward on the end of a string.

For the first time Carly really believed it was going to work; her store was going to be a success! Hugging her arms about herself, she scanned the crowded shop.

She wanted to run up and down the aisles, dance on the counter top, tell everyone. No, not everyone . . . *some*one. Matt. He had helped make it happen. But it was more than that. He'd understand.

She buried her head in a bundle of kite spools and tried to replace his soft half-smile and teasing, probing eyes with the more practical images of kites, string, and sales receipts. But when she stood up the handsome image was still there.

Her heart gave one sudden, clumsy lurch. That smiling face was over near the doorway, with that wonderful lean body attached, leaning comfortably against a new display of parafoil kites.

Her mouth flew open in surprise just as she was bombarded by four customers wanting out-of-stock kites, a stuck cash register, and a growing line of students wanting to pay for their kites and leave.

Matt wove his way through the crowd toward the register. He paused just long enough to dust a kiss across her cheek, then bent over to pick up a stack of paper bags and began filling one with a customer's purchases. He hummed as he worked and Carly worked silently beside him, her heart and mind playing a frantic game of Ping-Pong with one another.

And he was still there at six o'clock when he helped the three women usher the last customer out into the darkening street.

"Whew," Carly sighed, leaning tiredly against his shoulder.

Matt wrapped his arms about her, steadying her against him. "Yeah, life is a lot slower at the university." He grinned.

"And not nearly such a challenge, I bet!" Carly pushed a stray lock away from one eye and gave him a weary, teasing wink.

"Depends, I guess." Matt's voice took on a philosophical tone. "Depends on what you consider a challenge. For me, teaching is very much a challenge."

"Well, yes, of course it is," Carly answered softly, suddenly uncomfortable in the darkening shop.

She touched his arm lightly as Beth and Maria disappeared to straighten up the supply room. "Matt, today has been crazy. Thank you so much for helping."

He cupped her hand gently with his own and held it there against the dark hair of his arm. "Listen, Gypsy, I've made a fervent vow *never* to leave a damsel in distress. Especially one I can't seem to resist." He moved his hand upward and fingered a dark tendril near her ear, then gently looped it back, and Carly shivered beneath the whisper of his touch on her cheek.

His eyes touched her soul and Carly took a deep breath. It felt so good to have him near. *Too* good, she was beginning to realize. Her emotions had become entangled, and she wasn't at all sure she liked feeling so dependent on a man.

She shivered slightly and looked into his eyes.

"Well, Matt, I think that's it. I need to get this body upstairs and into a warm bath before the aches become ironed in."

"Oh?" Matt's brows lifted with the same suggestive overtones as his voice. "Well then perhaps it's too soon for me to leave?"

Carly bowed her head to hide the emotion she felt. "No, Matt—"

He cupped her chin with one hand and forced her to look at him. "What is it, Gypsy? Something is troubling you."

"You!" Carly blurted out, feeling the well of emotion fill her throat. "It's you, Matt Linton! You and me."

His hands fell away. "What's wrong?" he asked huskily.

"Matt, I want us to be honest with each other. I like you too much already for it to be any other way."

"That's usually best, Carly," he uttered darkly, leaning back against the counter.

"Good," she hurried on, locking the cash register and slipping the key into her pocket. "I think we're getting too close too quickly. We've got to be sensible, and careful before one of us gets hurt."

A muscle jumped in his jaw. "You're too late, Carly."

"Stop, Matt. Don't make this more difficult than it is." Her voice grew weaker. "I love being with you but I think we have to defuse some of the intensity between us. I have a business to get off the ground and it means everything to me right now. It requires a lot more of my energy and time than I've been able to give it recently."

Matt's eyes narrowed. "Because of me?"

Carly nodded.

"Then we'll just have to spend more days like today—working side by side at the store. One down. What other problems do you envision in our future?"

"Oh, Matt," Carly cried in exasperation. "See? Right there. I'd say, 'What else is bugging you?' and *you*, in the middle of this terrible fight, come up with 'What problems do you envision?' You and I are very, very different. Like night and day—"

"So I'll change my diction." Matt grinned crookedly. "But this is not a terrible fight, Carly. I've been in the middle of terrible fights."

"So have I, Matt. I had a peculiar adolescence. I spent half of it dodging bullets in the war my parents called a marriage. My brother's divorced. My best friend, Beth, is divorced. I . . . I have a few hang-ups, you might say, regarding serious relationships. They inevitably include commitments and disappointments and responsibilities that drive people crazy."

"Carly." Matt's hands stroked tenderly over the tense muscles in her shoulders. "Listen, Gypsy, now I understand a little better what's going on in that beautiful head of yours. Where that faraway look

93

comes from at the oddest moments. But don't you realize that our differences would never lead to that kind of relationship? You can't base your life on other people's mistakes, Carly, or—"

"Oh, Matt." Her voice trembled and she ran her hands lightly through his hair.

The supply-room door opened at that moment and Beth and Maria walked through. "We're leaving, boss lady." Beth laughed. "And I'm going to sleep for three days!"

Maria collected her things and in minutes the two left, bidding Carly and Matt a good evening.

When Carly focused back on Matt she noticed the tension had eased from his face. The interruption had been well timed, Carly thought, for each time Matt had touched her, her defenses withered until there was little left.

Carly smiled softly. "What a lousy way to thank you for the day."

Matt leaned over and kissed her lightly. "Yes, it was. But I'm going to systematically put everything you've just said on hold. And I'll show you somehow, I swear I will, how absolutely wrong you are. But in the meantime," he held her slightly apart and looked into her eyes, "may I ask you what I originally came to say when I walked into this place eight hours ago?"

Carly giggled at his plaintive request. "Of course you can. Speak. Ask."

"I want you to go out to dinner with me Saturday

night. Some old NASA friends of mine are in town for a kick-off fund-raising dinner. It's for Vic Clayton's Senate campaign."

"The astronaut? I heard he was running. This dinner must be a fancy do." Fancy, and serious, and filled with staid politicians all trying to impress one another, she thought. Filled with all those differences between her and Matt Linton that she wanted so much to forget.

"Well, yes, I guess so. It's at the Drake. Lots of former astronauts, hot-shot pilots, and the like—"

"Sounds like a cast party for *The Right Stuff*," Carly muttered, sorting her thoughts out as she spoke. Meeting Matt's friends was appealing in a way, but stepping into his other world would add just one more complication to the whole mess. And that kind of dinner was definitely not her cup of tea! "No . . . no, Matt. I don't think so."

"Why not, Carly?" Matt asked, hurt registering in his voice.

"Well . . . I just wouldn't fit in. I mean, I don't even have anything to wear to that kind of dinner. I don't have the right stuff," she laughed weakly.

But in the end Matt's pleading blue eyes and the enticing thought of meeting part of Matt's past weakened Carly's objections to the state of Jell-O. With a promise not to make any demands on her time until he rang her bell at seven-thirty Saturday night, Matt disappeared into the murky blackness of the summer night.

95

Beth brought over "the perfect dress" the next night—a cloud of apricot silk gathered into ethereal folds. "It's guaranteed to send them all back into space," she whispered conspiratorially, and Carly, with the dress flowing like shimmering water over her slender form, was inclined to agree. The neckline dipped and curved over the swell of her breasts, allowing a perfect "Elizabethan contour."

"Beth," Carly had pleaded, "isn't there some way we can yank this neckline up a bit?"

"Now, now—it's not nice to fool Mother Nature!" Beth had laughed. Then added ominously, "It's too late, my friend. You're on your own now."

"You're on your own, Carly West," she nervously told her reflection in the mirror as she waited for Matt to arrive on Saturday night. On your own, and that's how you like it—right? she asked herself. Well, remember that when you turn to putty the first time he touches you! She groaned aloud at the seething confusion of her emotions, the too-fast flutter of her pulse, the spots of color high on her cheekbones that no makeup could hide.

Smoothing her hands over the elegant fall of the silk, she steadied herself, then touched a hand to the loose knot of hair at the back of her neck. When the bell rang, she hurried to the back door, slipped the rose-colored shawl over her shoulders, and opened it to welcome Matt.

Matt was silent and still when he saw her, his eyes gone wide with approval and desire. Moonlight slipped over his shoulder and bathed her there before him, a lovely portrait in soft hues. "You're beautiful. I've never seen anyone so beautiful—"

"Stop, Matt!" she laughed, moving to stand close to him, her admonitions swept away by his nearness. "You'll make me blush and I'll clash with my dress." Tilting her head to one side, she smiled up at him. "I am glad you like it."

"You. It's you I like. All the different Carly Wests I'm getting to know. What did I do to get so lucky?"

She laughed deep in her throat, a strange mixture of embarrassment and arousal that filled her head with fantasy. "Stop it now." Slipping an arm through his, she leaned close. "Hadn't we better go?"

"Yes." He nodded, his eyes warm on her face. "Yes, I want to show you off. I want to introduce you to everyone I've ever known. Ever met. I want to watch you sip champagne and smile at strangers and move through a crowded room. And then I want to fill my arms with you and dance with you into the night." He had slipped an arm about her waist to draw her to him and suddenly he stopped, surprise filling his eyes. "You have your hair tied back!"

"It's called a chignon, sir . . ."

"Let it down," he coaxed softly. "Please?"

97

"No," she laughed, looking at him strangely. "No, Matt. This is my formal look, 'simple yet elegant'—"

"Let it down," he repeated, his hand lifting to her hair.

"Matt, stop!" She twisted away from his touch, then asked in a whisper. "Don't you like it?"

"Yes. You're beautiful. But the gypsy is . . . restrained somehow . . ."

Carly laughed nervously. "Well, maybe tonight I'm not a gypsy. And you're not a professor. Maybe tonight's just magic—"

Matt bit back his reply, shrugged the sudden tension from his shoulders and smiled. "I'll settle for magic. Let's go."

A valet whisked the car away, a doorman spun them through the entrance into a crystal fantasy, and they were at the Drake, stepping into a ballroom aglow with the light from sparkling chandeliers, the dais hung with red, white, and blue bunting, the centerpieces decorated with mums and miniature rockets.

"Nice and subdued. Just Nick's style," Matt laughed.

"It's wonderful," Carly breathed. There was an excitement in the air that blew away all her hesitations about coming.

"*You're* wonderful. Ready? Here comes some of the crew—"

"Hey, Linton!" "Lucky Linton, you old rogue!" A

phalanx of broad-shouldered, ruddy-cheeked men approached Matt and Carly.

"How ya doing, you old devil?" one man asked, slapping Matt on the shoulder.

"Still playing the professor? Like life in the ivory tower, old man? Hey, who is this gorgeous creature?" another old friend asked.

"Gentlemen—and I use the term most loosely—this is Carly West. Carly, these characters are Jerry, Craig, Jim, Barry, and Chief. And this distinguished, gray-haired gent over here is our own illustrious Vic Clayton, future senator from Illinois. Hey, Vic, good to see you!"

The men clasped hands warmly. "And good to see you, Sting. It has been too long. Glad you could make it!" He spoke the last words with one eye on Carly. Smiling, his complete attention soon moved toward her. "May I have your vote, ma'am?"

"Only if you promise *not* to call me 'ma'am,'" Carly laughed. "And even then, I want to read your position papers first."

"Vic Clayton—Carly West," Matt said. "And Vic, I'm warning you—don't tangle with this one . . . !"

"Okay, Sting. I'll leave it to you." He nudged his friend with a grin. "Now, folks, I guess I better go and behave like a candidate. Catch you all later."

"Sting?" Carly repeated to his retreating tux. One dark brow cocked quizzically above flashing

99

dark eyes and she narrowed a look at Matt Linton. "Did he call you . . . Sting?"

"Oh, it's nothing," Matt laughed. "Just an old, *old* nickname. It died years ago but Vic must have missed the wake. Time for champagne—I'll be back in a second."

"Foolish man! Never leave a beautiful woman alone, even for a second. He's gotten rusty with the passing years." It was Jerry, or Jim, Carly couldn't be sure which, but her confusion didn't put the slightest damper on her companion's conversation.

"So you're with Linton. He always did have a terrific eye. You from California?"

"No, Evanston. And are these compliments you're tossing out so freely?"

"Hell, yes! Ah . . . am I the first of Sting's old cronies you've met?"

"Most certainly."

"Well, ah, then I guess I had better slow down. Don't want to put a monkey wrench in the works."

"Are you an astronaut?" Carly asked slowly, fingering the delicate rose she'd been handed when they walked through the door.

"Pilot." He said the single word as if it explained everything.

Carly nodded as if she understood everything.

"Care to dance, Linton's lovely lady?"

"Fine . . ." They moved onto the already crowded dance floor and Carly pressed her partner for some answers.

"Say, why do you call Matt 'Sting'?"

"Sting. Short for Stinger. Or Sting Ray. Hasn't he told you about his cars . . . or anything?"

"No," Carly said hesitatingly. Colors and music and wonderful scents meshed in the background but Carly kept her attention riveted to the pilot's face, hoping to learn something about that part of Matt's life that was beyond her grasp. But her partner's face became impassive, as if he didn't want to be the one to divulge any information about Matt's past, so they danced to the pulsating beat of the music until Matt cut in.

"Where did you go without me, woman?" Matt asked.

"Right here, *Sting* . . ." She danced then within the curve of his arm, her body grazing his as she moved. She felt him tense, his body reacting to every movement of hers. "You know, Professor, I think I've been missing part of the story. Want to fill in some of the blanks?"

"It's an old story. Dull. Let's concentrate on the future, you and I. As the old philosopher says, 'What's past is past.' " He pulled her close and as he took her in his arms the music slowed. He held her gently, lovingly, his face nuzzled against her hair. The pervasive heat of his body made her tremble.

"Carly, do you know what you do to me?"

How could she pretend not to when he held her so close she could feel the beat of his heart? When

101

his very body heat melted away her defenses, her convictions, and left her emotions raw and exposed.

"It's no more than you do to me." Her voice was soft. "Every time I'm sure I can be sensible, and resist you, I'm wrong. I fail—"

"Good." His hand gently massaged the smooth bare skin of her back.

"No, it's *bad*, Professor. Bad. We're only going to get hurt, you and I—"

"I wouldn't hurt you, Carly. Never. You can trust me on that."

"I know you don't intend to, Matt," she whispered.

They danced until dinner, separating reluctantly to find their places at the huge round tables banked in snowy linen. Matt finally found their two engraved place cards and they settled down at the lovely table next to Craig and a dazzling blonde.

"Linda, honey," Craig drawled in a Houston-bred accent, "I want you to meet Matt and Carly. Matt's an old NASA buddy—reformed now, or so the story goes. Right, Sting?"

Purposely ignoring the remark, Matt graciously shook the young woman's hand and spoke seriously to Craig. "You know, Craig, if you ever get to Stanford, I'd love to show you around the campus. The lab facilities are terrific."

"No more rat traps, Sting? Remember that crate they had me testing? What, ten . . . twelve years ago was it? Whoo-ee, remember that? And that little dollie who worked evenings"—his eyelids flicked up and down like a snake's—"she was the one who liked—"

"Hey, there's a whole new world out there, Craig, believe it or not. And I'm a whole new man. Older and wiser, as the saying goes." His words were light but his eyes darkened dangerously.

"That's the story, buddy. I just think it's a damn waste of some fine material." He drawled the last word until it fairly dripped with innuendos. Then, turning slowly to Carly, he grinned. "Did Linton ever tell you he holds the land speed record?"

"Cars?" Carly asked hopefully, although Matt's fierce blush told her instantly it was nothing so ordinary.

"Nope. Not cars, although he played with them too. That's how he got his nickname, right, buddy? Had this shiny little red Corvette Stingray, always polished brighter than a ship's brass. Why, we'd watch for it—"

"Craig," Matt warned, but his interruption was waved away by Craig's dramatic gestures.

"Why, we'd see it flashin' by out of the complex right around the middle of the afternoon, some dollie in the front seat, and we'd know the record was about to bite the dust again!"

"That's enough, Craig," Matt growled, his eyes icy blue. "It's over. Dead and gone. Let it lie, man."

"What? Hey, we old NASA buddies always reminisce." He took a long drink of his scotch. "No harm meant . . ."

"No harm done, Craig. Let's just can it, okay?" Matt's hands were clenched, his knuckles as white as the cloth beneath them. But his voice was low and even. He turned to Carly. "Want to catch a breath of air?"

Carly nodded, avoiding Matt's eyes. Her lips formed a thin, white-edged line; her coal-black eyes were narrowed into slits. She preceded him silently to the wide french doors opening onto a stone veranda. The cool evening breeze did little to assuage the heated turmoil coursing through her veins. Matt's foot barely touched the pavement when she turned on him.

"How dare you? How—No, that's not the question at all. *Who are you? That's* the question!" Laughing bitterly, she held her head in disbelief. "You must have thought I was pretty funny. The little naive kite-store girl who thinks you're this wonderful, learned, serious professor. I mean . . ." Tears sprang to her eyes. "I even *call* you 'Professor'!"

"And it's the sweetest thing I've ever heard."

"Oh? You like it better than *Sting?* Why didn't you ever tell me? These days . . . and weeks . . . you say 'Trust me, Carly,' and I do. I did. How could you?"

"Because *I'm* falling in love with you, Carly West. And I was afraid. Afraid of what the past could do.

Afraid of *this!* I haven't been Sting in years. Maybe I never really was. But fifteen years ago it ruined my life. *I* ruined my life, my marriage—"

"What? All this was going on while you were married? You . . . you did that?" She backed away from him, her eyes huge and frightened as a deer's.

"Carly—" Quickly Matt stepped closer, blocking her escape with his body and drawing her down on a round stone bench with hands that were as cold as ice. "Carly, yes, I made a mistake. But I was a kid. We both were, with not the slightest idea of what marriage was or should be. I was the hot-shot scientist. NASA grabbed me straight from grad school. Dropped me and Jenna in this movie set they called a life, complete with big houses, big bucks. Fast living, fast women. Hell, Jenna and I were two young kids from Apple Valley, we didn't know how to handle it. We thought we were doing okay." His laugh was harsh and full of regret. "Sting was the image I thought came with the job. I worked too hard; played too hard. I was young and it was so easy there. A look, a smile. That's all it took. I thought I possessed some incredible sexual power; I didn't know it was only the time and the place.

"But it all fell apart. We had two kids by then, but nothing else. Jenna took them back to her parents in California; I took a good, hard look in the mirror —and in my soul—shook myself off, pulled myself together, and accepted a teaching position at Stanford." His handsome face creased in a wry grin. "It's so easy to blame—the situation, the time, the intensity of the work. Me. Jenna. But I finally came around to seeing the folly of doing that. It happened. People were hurt. But the pieces have been slowly glued back together.

"Stanford was good to me. My credentials were still impeccable, believe it or not, and they wanted me. But those were lonely years. I've been lonely for a long time."

Carly didn't know he had loosened his hold until she felt his hands moving gently up and down her bare arms. "I hurt you, too. I'm sorry."

Blinking, she looked down to where his hands stroked her. There were the faint red pressure marks of his grip. "It's all right. I . . . I think I overreacted." The worry line between her dark brows deepened and she bit her lip. "Did I, Matt? Is that all it was?"

"Yes, darlin'. That's all. I'm still me."

"You frighten me. I know so little. You have a whole past, a whole life I've no part of."

"That's true for everyone. We all come together as strangers, until we love." Crooking his finger beneath her chin, he tilted her face up until he could look into her eyes. Then he bent and kissed her gently, deeply. "Isn't that true, Carly West?"

"Yes . . ." Carly looked into his eyes and her lips curled in a slow smile. "But it . . . it will take me a while to digest all of this. To figure out Matt from

Sting. I don't know whether to be angry . . . or hurt . . . or—"

"Or what?" There was a keen, sexy angle to his grin, to the feel of his body as it pressed against hers.

Carly's body registered it instinctively. Her frown line reappeared. "Matt Linton—don't you try any of those 'Sting' tricks on me."

"Never!" He rubbed his cheek against hers. "But I was thinking how odd this all is. If you had asked me a few minutes ago, I would have said I was damn sorry you had to hear any of this. Had to ever find out. But now"—he shifted his weight, almost as if he were shifting gears—"now I think I'm kind of glad. It's as if I were trying to keep part of myself locked away, under guard. Now I'm free."

"Free to what . . . ?" Carly breathed.

"Free to fall in love," he whispered, smiling at her from a new depth in his piercing blue eyes.

"Oh . . . damn—"

"Does that mean you'd rather dance?"

"Definitely!"

Back in the ballroom the tables had been cleared, dinner was over, and coffee was being served. The band began playing slow, sweet jazz.

Matt held Carly lightly, their bodies barely touching as they swayed in tandem, but Carly trembled as if the very ground beneath her shook. A solid seven on the Richter scale.

Matt tightened his hold, drawing her closer, and

Carly felt a hot shock of recognition as their bodies touched length to length.

He danced well, controlling her with unconscious ease, and Carly had nowhere to focus her concentration but on the feel of him against her. She felt the subtle play of his muscles beneath his tuxedo and his splayed hand burned through the watery silk at the small of her back. She was trapped in flame between the touch of his hand and the press of his body.

If only, her mind began to wander, if only she were somewhere else. If only she could suspend time for a brief moment and enjoy all of Matt Linton. If only she could slowly peel the jacket off his shoulders, slowly unbutton the buttons along the front of his shirt and part the fabric to touch his warm flesh. Slide her hand along his chest and push her fingers through the rough springy hairs. And pull the shirt off slowly until he stood bare-chested and she could trace the curve of muscles across his upper arms and shoulders and back and . . .

Carly missed a step, stumbled, and Matt caught her tightly around the waist to steady her.

"Are you all right?"

"Fine!" she answered too quickly. A flood of heat suffused her cheeks and throat and the curves of her breast revealed by the plunging silk. Her eyes flew to his face and widened in panic.

Matt's eyes were clearly tracing the spreading path of her blush. But instead of embarrassment,

Carly felt an unexpected, startling leap of arousal. "Matt . . . I . . ."

"Do you want to go somewhere else?" His voice was low and seductive.

"Do you?" Carly asked in a whisper.

"Yes."

Her hand fluttered nervously to her throat. "Then we'd better not."

A low, husky laugh sounded in his throat. "Why not? The time seems right." Temptation gleamed in his deep-blue eyes and his look was a caress.

"I don't know what to make of you, Matt Linton."

"You could make me a happy man," he whispered.

"Yes, but would I be smiling in the morning?"

"Hell yes! I guarantee it. Trust me."

"Ah, maybe that's where the problem lies."

"That again?" he growled. "Fine. Then let's stay here and dance."

Carly opened her mouth, closed it again, and stared at him. "Matt, you make me crazy. I'm normally a sane, even-tempered person—"

"I won't hold that against you." He grinned, gathering her back into his arms.

"Matt—" she hissed. "Dance!"

"How nice of you to ask," he laughed, guiding her lightly across the floor. "You know, don't you, Carly West, that you are by far the most beautiful woman here tonight? The most beautiful woman I've ever seen . . ."

"Matt—"

"My sky gypsy." Circling his hand over her back, he set her nerves tingling. "I love the feel of you, the way I get lost in those dark, shining eyes. Your hair as dark as endless space—" Reaching up, before she knew what he was about to do, he pulled loose the single pin that held the knot in place. Her hair spilled loose across his hand and down her back.

"Matt, I told you not to do that!" Carly stormed, trying desperately to keep her voice below the sound of the music. "You can't have everything you want any more!"

"There's only one thing I want. You." He smiled and spun her tightly against him until her hair flew wild and free, and the night drew them into its swirling folds.

CHAPTER SIX

Matt fumbled with the buttons of his shirt, the urgency of his desire making him awkward.

"Here," Carly laughed softly, more tender than teasing. "Here, Professor, let me." She pushed his hands away. They fell like stones to his sides as they stood before one another. Her small bedroom was filled with shadows curling about their fervent, eager bodies.

Matt's chest rose and fell, and his breathing was rough and hoarse.

Before she touched the first button, Carly lay her hand flat against his chest. Watched it rise and fall with his breath. Felt the heat of his flesh burning through the thin shirt.

"Carly . . ." he groaned, stretching her name into a sound of pure delight.

"Do you know how I've wanted to do just that all night, Matt?" she asked. "Just to touch you as simply as that, as if it were my right?"

He smiled. "I do know. I think that is why I loosened your hair, although I knew it would make you angry. Just to believe I had that right."

"And your heart . . . I feel your heart pounding. I like knowing I do that to you."

"That's not half of what you do, Gypsy," he laughed, the sound rumbling in his chest. "Slide your hand down a bit . . ."

"Oh, no. I won't be hurried."

Groaning, Matt buried his face in the dark cloud of her hair. He nipped at the tender, fleshy pad of her earlobe and slipped his hot, moist tongue into her ear. His breath awoke shivers that prickled and danced across her skin.

Carly giggled deep in her throat. Her breasts ached for his touch. Her nipples were hard, throbbing pinpoints of desire. She was swept by an insane urge to curve against him, to feel her fevered flesh on his. She wanted to make love with him again, to touch again every inch of his body, to peel away any last layers between them that kept them strangers.

Slipping one small white button through its buttonhole, Carly parted his shirt and slid her hand into the opening. The warm flesh beneath welcomed her touch. She heard the sharp intake of his breath and smiled. Slowly, her concentration focused on the widening V of exposed, bronzed skin,

112

she unbuttoned his shirt completely. Tugged it free of his slacks. Spread the white cotton wide open and brushed the backs of her fingers against his chest. "Do you know what I like about you, Matt Linton? Shall I tell you?"

"Tell me."

"You have the courage to be tender, to let me know I move you. To let me see what's been hidden in your heart."

Something seemed to flicker in the sky blue of his eyes, but he whispered, "No doubt about that, darlin'." Then his eyes shifted back and focused on a point beyond Carly's shoulder. A slow sexy smile curved his lips. "Look, we've got company."

"What?" Quickly Carly glanced over her shoulder, then shared his smile. Her large oval mirror, pinioned in its antique frame, held their reflection: the merger of two lovers, standing together in a gentle prelude to love.

She watched, her eyes following the reflected path of his eager hands as they slipped over the apricot silk. Watched as he loosened the few fasteners and, her vision eclipsed for a moment as she lifted her arms, slipped the dress over her head. Dark waves of silken hair lapped her bare shoulders. She watched his hands move like dark liquid shadows on her skin as he slipped them beneath the waistband of her slip and sent it shimmering in folds down over her slender legs.

And she watched herself standing there, glistening bare and quivering beneath his touch. A vibrating thrill ran down her straight spine and rippled across her naked torso.

"Touch me," she implored, her voice as weak as her knees.

"I couldn't stop if I wanted to, darling," Matt growled. "I'm a bear to your honey."

Carly felt the dizzying caress of his hands in pure desire as they moved over the taut skin covering her breastbone then circled the tender swelling of her breasts. Her own slender back shielded her view, but she felt his hands cup her fullness, his thumbs tracing ever-narrowing circles around her nipples as if the exquisite ache of her desire guided his touch. And as he touched her straining nibs, she gave a soft little cry, the rippling, rippling waves of her desire flooding her with swift abandon.

Too quickly his hands left her breasts, snatching her breath away. "No . . . no . . . don't stop, my love," she gasped.

But he touched her shoulders instead, turning her around until her spine bisected his chest, and she faced the dark beveled glass.

She saw his smile glimmer above the crown of her head. His eyes burned with hunger for her, devouring her nakedness with a deep-blue blaze. Again his hands cupped her breasts. He petted and stroked her, catching her nipples between thumb and forefinger and rolling the swollen, aching tips in quick breath-catching tugs. Rapt, Carly let her weight fall back upon him. Her lids drooped heavily over her eyes. But still she watched as his hands roamed her body. It was as though the mirror magnified each sensation; each touch became almost unbearably erotic. She trembled.

"Matt . . . come, let's lie down. Come, come to the bed—"

"Now who's hurrying, my gypsy?" he murmured. "I love to look at you. You are so beautiful."

Reaching up and behind her, Carly wrapped her arms around his neck like silken ropes. Her body began to sway against his, the creamy length of her back and flank rubbing against him with sensual languor.

Waiting suddenly became impossible.

Gathering her into his arms, Matt took two steps to the side of the bed and tossed her onto the quilt. Grinning down at her, he pulled off his shirt, his muscles flexing and rippling beneath his skin. He gleamed bronze gold in the dusk. He unbuckled his belt and let it dangle to the floor. Unzipping his slacks, he peeled them down over lean hips and let them slide to the floor. Then he hooked his thumbs in the waistband of his briefs, and drew them down as well. A glint of amusement flickered through the desire in his blazing eyes. "So much for hiding the fact that you move me, Gypsy," he laughed, the sound curling around her like smoke.

Carly opened her arms wide, and Matt fell into them. She kissed him gently, lovingly, and Matt dusted kisses across her warm trembling flesh. He felt his loins begin to burn, and knew he wanted to love her again . . . wanted to stop time and love her on through dark and daylight, and banish forever any threat to their happiness. And in a moment he began to love her again.

A soft sliver of sunlight slid across Carly's sleeping body and rested in a wavy pattern across her legs. Somewhere deep beneath the harshness of waking, she registered its warmth and stirred softly, still reluctant to relinquish her dreams to morning. But as reality seeped its way in, memory returned and a soft smile curved her lips. Matt . . . Matt and Carly. The two tossed and entwined in the fabric of a fairy tale. . . .

Without raising an eyelid, Carly reached over to touch the warm flesh of her lover.

The chill emptiness jarred her fully awake.

"Matt?" Her eyes, wide open now, swept over the empty half of the bed, then scanned the open, sunwashed room. "Matt?"

She lifted up on one elbow, bolstering herself with a pillow, and the thin sheet slipped down beneath the curve of her breasts, her skin pale as milk in the morning light. Then her dark searching eyes found the large sheet of paper, filled with a hasty masculine scrawl, that was pinned to the edge of the pillow.

My darling Mother Hubbard, your cupboard was bare. Gone hunting for hot croissants and marmalade. Rest, my sleeping beauty. I'll return with a kiss,

Matt

Carly unpinned the note and held it up to the light, studying it. Her upturned eyes were filled with amazement. Here she was falling madly in love with a man whose handwriting she had never seen before. Whose life was a mystery. Whose past —and future—seemed cloaked in shadow. . . .

But no! That wasn't to be dealt with today. Today was bound too tightly in the silken threads of their lovemaking to allow for intrusions. Carly sank back into the cool whiteness of the pillow, closed her eyes, and invited her sensual, lovely dreams of Matt to return to fill her head . . . until he returned to fill her arms.

She must have slipped back into sleep, for the tapping at the door had become insistent and harsh before it registered clearly in her consciousness. Carly jerked awake, momentarily startled by the knocking on the door. Then her head cleared, and her face lit with a welcoming smile. Matt must have returned with breakfast.

"Hurry up, Linton! I'm starving!"

The door clicked open and shut again and hesitant footsteps traced her voice into the secluded bedroom at the end of the hall.

Carly's mouth flew open, but no sound came out.

A tall, youthful figure leaned against the doorway, broad shoulders filling the space, blond hair sun-streaked and wavy and a bit too long, like the kids in the soft-drink commercials for the Pepsi generation. His face was smooth, his skin appropriately tanned, but he was not smiling. Instead his mouth was pulled firm into an expression of righteousness, veiling the brief flicker of embarrassment that Carly had seen in the clear blue eyes.

"Wh . . . who . . ." Carly stuttered as her breath pumped through her body in ragged spurts. Clenching the sheets until her knuckles matched their whiteness, she forced a deep breath and leveled a hard look at the intruder. "Who are you and what are you doing in my bedroom?" The words arrowed through the still room.

His eyes remained riveted to her face, his shoulders lounging arrogantly against the doorframe. "I'm Dave Linton. I'm looking for my father. And *you* invited me in . . . or so I thought." His gaze and voice were cold. "One of Dad's buddies at the university said I might find him around here."

Carly's initial fear gave way to surprise as her eyes traveled slowly over the young man's features: the strong, well-built limbs beneath the faded jeans and work shirt, the well-shaped head and long, firm nose, and those same sky-blue, see-right-through-you blue eyes. Matt's son. Yes. But how could he have a son so old? Why, he seemed nearly *her* age. . . .

Carly shifted beneath the sheets, and smiled tentatively. "Hello, Dave. I'm Carly West. And yes, your dad will be here soon, I suspect. I'd . . . uh . . . offer to shake hands, but"—she glanced self-consciously down at the outline of her body beneath the chin-high sheet and blushed—"but under the circumstances I think you should wait in the living room for a minute and we can become properly introduced in there." She smiled, expecting him to turn and leave.

But Dave Linton didn't budge, nor did his eyes shift from their narrowed gaze on her face. "Have you known him long? My dad, I mean—" Beneath his words was an accusing tone that wiped the smile off Carly's face.

"No, not long. Well, since he's been here at Northwestern. He's . . . he has helped me get some business over at the university for my kite store."

"Oh. A payback then." His tone was flat, coldly matter-of-fact.

Carly's eyes blackened with sudden anger. "Turn around. Right now!"

The sharp command spun the young man around, and in one quick movement Carly grabbed her robe and wrapped it tightly around her. "Now sit down. There!" She pointed to the end of the bed. "Since you don't seem to want to fool with the usual decent formalities, I'll just set you straight, fast!"

119

Nervously pushing the hair out of his eyes, Dave Linton sank obediently onto the edge of the bed.

"Now, Dave, I don't know why you're here or what you want, but you have absolutely no right to start throwing nasty innuendos around my house. Especially about things of which you know nothing! Is that clear?"

The young man nodded, staring at her in silent amazement. Though he was not much younger than she, he felt as chastened as a small boy by this woman's anger. Deserved anger, he admitted to himself, his arrogance crumbling into apology. "Sure. I'm sorry. It's just that, well . . . one never knows with Dad."

"*I* know!" She fixed him with a steady gaze. Though questions flashed across her troubled mind, she was damned if she was going to let this puppy see the uneasiness he had caused. "Now I'd like very much to turn this conversation to a more relevant subject. You."

"Me?" Color stained his cheeks at this unexpected turn of events.

Carly let a smile escape. "Yes, you. Listen, your father is a good man, Dave. I like him. And I'd like to know something about his son."

The blue-edged morning slipped in through the small scrubbed windowpanes and coated the room in innocent sunshine. Dave looked at Carly, shrugged, and smiled. "Maybe I should apologize, then go out and start again—"

"Consider it done. Apologies accepted. Hassle forgotten. Are you going to be in town long?"

"No. I was on my way up to the upper peninsula with some buddies. We have a cabin rented. And . . . well . . . thought I'd better stop and say hello."

His words came reluctantly and it was clear to Carly that it was not because of her, but because Dave Linton wasn't wild about saying hello to his father. But she hadn't the faintest idea why.

"Oh, well I'm sure he'll be happy to see you."

"Yeah. Sure. Like the bubonic plague." He laughed a small, thin insecure laugh that held echoes of a past that was lost to Carly.

She fingered the soft quilt and watched Dave's eyes as he spoke. They wandered about the small room, then met hers.

"My father's quite a teacher, huh?" Catching Carly's warning look, he hastily continued, "I mean for the kids . . . in the classroom. People say he's a pretty hot professor. Some buddies of mine took his class at Stanford—"

"You've never heard him lecture?"

"Oh, sure. Lots of times! But never in a classroom." His joke fell flat and lay like a rock between them. Dave shrugged uncomfortably. "Actually, my father didn't lecture me a lot. He wasn't home enough to do that. Left that to Mom. But that was his *first* life, you know. His NASA life. People . . .

121

well, Mom . . . other people . . . they say he's different now. . . ."

"You don't believe them?"

"Oh, I'm sure you can teach an old dog new tricks and all that—" Dave's gray-edged gaze shifted beyond Carly and out the open window. One side of his mouth curved slowly into a curious smile. "Trouble is, Dad already knew all the tricks. Nothing left to learn. . . . Oh, shit!" He slapped the soft surface of the bedclothes suddenly and dust motes danced in the stream of sunlight. "I don't know why I started throwing all this at you. Dad and I lost a few years way back when." He looked at her long and steady. "And neither of us has had much interest in patching 'em up. Holes were too big, I guess. I don't see him much in California, although we do make stabs at getting together now and then. Somehow it always falls flat. I guess I thought a meeting on neutral ground . . . maybe we'd get a clearer look at each other. Hell, it probably doesn't matter anyhow. . . ." His voice drifted off.

Carly had listened with a chill walking up her arms. Her chest felt bound by some invisible chain, winding tighter with each word. The enormous mass of days that were Matt Linton's past swam before her mind's eye—a dark cloud that blocked the sunlight. A storm rising in her heart.

She was saved from mumbling some hollow reply by a great gusting up the back stairs and the sound of the door being flung wide.

"Breakfast, my love!" Matt sang as he breezed through the doorway, his arms filled with bakery boxes bulging at the seams, and the sweet odor of butter and yeast clinging to the warmed air around him.

Dave turned toward his father but didn't speak, barely moved.

Matt stopped just inside the door, the smile wiped clean away and replaced by a look of total and undisguised astonishment. Then his eyes darkened and Carly could see the cords in his neck jump, then tighten into a rigid line.

She was instantly saddened, for both father and son, and groped for a way to save them from this embarrassment, from meeting here, in *her* bedroom, from the tangle of emotions that twisted their faces.

"Matt, Dave came looking for you . . ." Her words hung like thin, meaningless threads in the charged air. Unheard.

"What the hell are you doing here?"

"Just passing through." Dave's voice was laced with well-worn insolence, and Matt's jaw clenched.

"Passing through Carly's bedroom?"

His voice chilled Carly's blood. It was a stranger's voice, cold, and iced with threat and sarcasm.

"Matt—" she implored, her eyes begging him to be gentle. "Matt, Dave was sent over by someone at the university. He doesn't have much time and just wanted to say hello. We had a nice little talk, waiting for you to get back. Now, why don't you two go into the kitchen and put on a pot of coffee and I'll just . . ."

"No need, Carly. I'm sure Dave can't stay now. I'll talk to him later."

"I might not be around later."

The two men looked at one another long and silently in the slanted light of morning. Father and son. A myriad of raw emotions passed through the small space between them. Carly waited for some acknowledgment, some response, her heart begging Matt to be the one to speak, the one to reach out. But the silence was too thick, too overwhelming.

Finally Dave spoke. "Sorry, Dad. Lousy timing, eh?" He winked with false camaraderie, and Matt bristled. Rising from the bed, Dave faced Carly. "Sorry again, Carly. It was nice talking to you, though, and I hope we'll meet again." Then in the same level tone he faced his father. "Distance doesn't seem to change anything any more than time. Same ol' Pop. Well, too bad. See ya."

"Damn right you'll see me. You come to *my* apartment tonight, David. Seven o'clock."

"Don't hold your breath, Dad . . ."

"David, you be there! Understand?"

The two men glared at each other in cold silence for a moment, and then Dave turned and was gone, leaving a draft in the warmed air that caused Carly to shiver beneath the soft fabric of her robe.

124

She stared at Matt in disbelief. "Matt—that was your son!"

"Oh? He introduced himself then? Good of him!" The icy tones were now leveled at her. "He had no right to barge in here like that. And sit as if he belonged there on the end of your bed!"

"Matt, you're not making sense." Softly she rose and moved closer to him. She tried to touch him but he backed away and dropped the boxes and bags clumsily onto the quilt. She could sense his pain, and again her hand went out to touch him, comfort him. "He seemed like a nice kid, Matt," she whispered.

He shrugged off her hand. "Kid, hell! He's nearly *your* age, Carly!"

So that was it, or at least part of this strange jumble of emotion. "Matt, I thought we had settled all of that. Age is a silly, meaningless barrier; it doesn't matter at all—"

"—not until I see you sitting next to him like that." Matt's voice softened slightly. "Listen, I know in my *head* it doesn't matter, but my *heart*'s a different story. It shocked me to hell to see the two of you looking like such a cute couple . . . and that damn cock-sure attitude of Dave's! It was plastered all over his face. He *liked* sitting there with you. *Liked* having me *see* him sitting there—"

"No, Matt. I think you're overreacting. That wasn't it at all! I think he doesn't know *how* to face you, so that's just a mask he puts on. Dave told me a little about your, ah, disagreements in the past—"

Matt shot her a narrowed look. "That's the past."

Carly persisted, her own emotions churning now. "Well, it may be the past, but that's a part of you, too, Matt Linton! And he mentioned things, by the way, that I don't understand, that I don't know a thing about . . . things you haven't told me!" There was an accusation in her tone which she hadn't *meant* to be there, but couldn't control.

Matt plucked it out immediately and flung it back at her. "Didn't know you needed a complete bio before we could make love."

"Matt, stop this!" Carly's anger was edged with a wild, fluttering panic. "Stop being so damn stubborn about this. Your son comes to see you and you don't even talk to him! And now you're somehow making *me* the scapegoat for the whole damn mess that doesn't make any sense to me in the first place!" Tears stung her eyes and her lips quivered.

Matt looked at her, the muscles jumping along the hard line of his jaw, then he walked slowly across the room and stared blindly out the window. "You're right," he whispered, his voice hoarse with strain. "It doesn't make any sense. I don't know why it hurt me so to see him here, but it did. That's all. It did. He shouldn't have come here like that . . . unexpected, unannounced." Unannounced, and dragging the unwelcome past in with him, Matt thought miserably within the heat of his anger.

"Well maybe he shouldn't have come without calling, but if it meant a chance to patch things up, couldn't *you* have used the opportunity better?"

It sounded like a reproach, and Matt's eyes darkened dangerously. "Carly, you don't know a thing about it."

"That's right. I don't know about your past. And whose fault is that? Whose fault is it that the man I make wonderful, fiery love with is someone I don't understand at all. You don't open up to me, Matt, don't tell me about yourself. I find out everything about your past from strangers at fancy dinners or if your son happens to walk through my door! Matt, I can't read your heart—"

"That's not true!" he denied vehemently. "You have my *whole heart*, Carly. As for the past, well . . . it's past and done; I didn't think it would matter to us now!"

"Maybe it doesn't, Matt . . . but maybe, just maybe, you need to trust me enough to share it. For something that doesn't matter, it certainly still seems capable of causing you a lot of pain—"

"Which is exactly why I don't want it to touch you!"

"Oh, thanks! You think I'm so delicate—such a fragile flower—that I can't know *all* of you and still love you?" She shook her head, spilling tears in all directions. "Maybe I don't know *anything* about you . . . and maybe you don't really know me."

Her crying made him crazy, filled him with that

127

same feeling of helplessness and self-loathing that had tormented him all those years ago. He swung out blindly. "Carly, sometimes I don't know what the hell you want! You're the one who shies away at any mention of commitment—"

"Oh no," she shouted back, "don't you try to turn this whole mess into something that's *my* fault! I think . . . well, *I* think *you're* scared! You're not sure of your own feelings and somehow Dave's appearance triggered a whole barrel of insecurities. You don't really know if you're angry at him or me or . . . or yourself!"

"That's enough, Carly." His voice was icy.

They glared at each other like two tigers ready to pounce. Then Matt turned and stalked toward the door. "Damn. Maybe Dave's right. Maybe nothing has changed . . ."

"And just what does *that* mean? Matt, stop! Don't you dare walk out that door. Matt . . . Sting! . . . I'm not through yet!"

Matt glanced back at her over his shoulder. "Have some breakfast, Carly," he drawled with maddening calm. "Maybe things will make more sense on a full stomach."

Carly reached down, tore the top off a box, and twisted her fingers around a still-warm croissant. "Matt, don't walk out on me—"

And she hurled the flaky pastry after him just as the door clicked shut. It fell to the floor with a light thud.

"Damn you, Matt Linton. Well, you just go!" she sputtered, her dark eyes brimming with tears.

Carly sank back on the tangled spread, took a bite of a croissant, and let the tears run freely down her cheeks.

CHAPTER SEVEN

Three days later Carly was out in the parking lot behind her store loading kites into the borrowed van. Her T-shirt clung to her breasts and back, her jeans soaked up the sun's rays like a sponge, and her hair wisped in damp tendrils around her face. Carly was thoroughly miserable.

Matt had not come back.

Her anger had dissolved into a loneliness so intense that she thought it must be visible, like mumps or the chicken pox. She ached every place his hand had ever touched her. And would never touch her again. How had she ever let it go so far, she wondered during the long sleepless nights. She knew better. Knew it wouldn't work, couldn't last. Knew, damn it all, better than to fall in love. But that's exactly what she had done. There was no denying it now. Now when it was all over.

Tears burned her eyes and she leaned against the open door of the van, her face buried in the crook of her arm.

"Love," she groaned. "What a mess it is! Just as I knew it would be!" She sniffed loudly for punctuation. "Well, don't act so surprised, Carly West. You, the sane, careful, sensible one. What foolishness to lose your heart to a man with a life as complicated as Clark Kent and Superman. All for a pair of sky-blue eyes, the gentlest smile. A touch like fire. Oh-h-h—" This time her groan was tainted with desire and frustration.

The sound of Maria's footsteps at the back door startled her. Muttering furiously, she straightened her slim shoulders, tossed her head, and slammed the heavy van door shut.

"Enough! Chalk it up to one of life's major disasters, and get on with things. Besides, he's not your type. You're better off this way! Business is booming —" She tossed her notes into the front seat on the passenger side. "You've got your life back in your own hands." She pulled the keys free from the jumble inside her purse. "And now you can be your own sane, sensible, happy self again!"

Maria stood just inside the door watching Carly. She frowned and shook her head. Carly had been talking to herself a lot these past few days. In the distance, she saw Carly square her shoulders and walk toward her.

"Maria? Oh, there you are. I just wanted you to know I'm on my way. The lecture's at ten and then—"

The sharp ring of the telephone cut her off. Maria hurried inside and answered it. She listened for a moment, then held it toward Carly. "It's Professor Linton, Carly. He—"

"Tell him I'm not here," Carly insisted. "Tell him I've already left for the campus."

"Carly, don't be foolish. Why—"

"No. Please, Maria. Tell him I'm not here."

Maria finally complied, her regret and disapproval clear in her voice and on her face. She repeated the message twice, most reluctantly, then dropped the phone back into its cradle.

"Carly, what has happened? This isn't like you, dear. Where is my old sane, happy Carly?"

"I am happy!" she snapped back. "Don't you know happy when you see it?" She turned a wide smile on Maria. "See? I'm happy! Now, don't worry. 'Bye."

She drove the two-lane highway toward campus, her mind pinned on her lecture. To let her thoughts drift was dangerous; they swarmed immediately to Matt's face like bees to honey. She couldn't even play the radio because a love song made her weep. A replay of "The Way We Were" could flood the van. Damn! Think only of business, Carly West!

That's why she almost didn't see Matt's car. He was heading toward her at breakneck speed on the opposite side of the road. He passed her, then spun in a wide U-turn and drew up alongside the van. Carly gunned the engine but the old van only shuddered and groaned and continued to chug along at a steady forty-five miles per hour.

Matt's little car pulled steadily closer.

Carly snatched a glance out her side mirror and her heart jumped up into her throat.

Matt held loosely to the steering wheel with one hand, his attention clearly divided between the road ahead and her. His eyes blazed with fierce determination. His jaw was set and a keen, exultant smile curved his lips. He edged the car closer, nudging the van toward the side of the road. He looked like a hunter, a wolf on the scent—and Carly felt the nip at her heels.

An oncoming car appeared over the rise of the road ahead. There! Now he'd have to stop. But he didn't! Stubbornly he hugged the middle of the road, refusing to let her escape. He'd be killed! Scrunched . . . pulverized!

Carly braked to a stop way off on the shoulder.

Matt slid to a halt just in front of her.

His lean frame unfolded from the car and with maddening nonchalance he walked to the side of the van.

"Hi, Gypsy."

"Are you crazy? What do you think you are doing?" Her hands gripped the steering wheel in white-knuckled panic. Her black eyes sparked. "Are you crazy?"

"No. I'm in love."

"You *are* crazy. Who walked out the door? Who left whom? You! You didn't call. And now you almost kill us both!"

"I needed time to think," he answered calmly, as if having this conversation through a van window on the side of the road was a perfectly natural thing to do.

"Well, so did I. You did us both a favor," Carly yelled, her voice rising more than she had intended it to do. "Now it's over, which is just as well, since it had to end sooner or later, and we both knew that—"

"I didn't—don't—know any such thing, darlin'."

"That's because you are the most pigheaded, stubborn, impossible man—in addition to being crazy."

"Crazy in love. That's no crime." He grinned, reaching through the half-opened window to stroke her cheek.

Carly tried to roll the window up but Matt was too fast. His hand snaked in, lifted the lock, and yanked the door open.

"Come on out, Carly. I want to talk to you."

"I am not getting out of this van. I have business to attend to—"

"We have more important things to attend to, you and I. Come on out."

"No. We're going to get into an accident stopping this way on the side of the road."

"Then follow me to a place where we can talk safely."

"Forget it! I have nothing to say to you," she protested.

"If you don't follow me, Gypsy, I'll just keep running you off the road until you do talk to me." He flashed a mischievous smile at her. "I'm a persistent man," he added.

"All right," she relented. "I suppose I can spare a minute or two."

Carly followed Matt down the highway to a.small private airport. She pulled up beside him at the front of the gleaming fuselage of a trim Lear jet and jumped out of her van. "Okay, Matt, talk," Carly said peremptorily, folding her arms across her chest.

"I will, but first get in the plane, Carly," Matt said matter-of-factly.

"Matt, this has gone far enough! The joke's over. I am *not* getting in that plane!"

"Yes, you are, Gypsy," Matt insisted, wrapping his arm firmly around her shoulders. "Even if I have to sling you over my shoulder. I'll do it, you know. . . ."

"I'll . . . I'll scream. I'll kick! I'll make you sorry you ever laid eyes on me."

135

"Impossible. I told you—I love you."

"Matt, let me go. Please."

"Did you hear me, Carly? Did you—"

"Yes," she croaked, "I heard you!" Breathe, Carly, she intoned silently. Breathe, and think. . . .

"Then why don't you answer me?" He curved over her, blacking out the sight of the plane, the sunlight, everything but his hard, tantalizing body, the demand and desire on his handsome face. "Answer me."

"I don't want to. I . . . I don't have anything to say."

"That's why I'm taking you away. So we'll have time to say what needs to be said between us."

"No, I don't want to, Matt."

"Why not?" he asked softly, his eyes searching hers for the answer she was afraid to speak. "Tell me, Carly, do you love me? Tell me . . ." he whispered against her lips as his mouth lowered to hers in a hungry kiss.

Her body was incapable of deceit. Her lips parted beneath his, her mouth opening to the sweet, hot, deliberate slide of his tongue into the secret recesses of her mouth, her very soul. She could do nothing, wanted to do nothing but yield and affirm his love. But as he drew away, her lips still clinging like snagged silk to his, fear nagged at her heart and closed her throat. She looked away.

"Gypsy, if you can tell me you don't love me, then

136

I will let you go. Now. Forever. But if you can't, then, goddamn it, I'm going to fight for you."

"And . . . and who do you think you're fighting, Matt Linton?" Carly stammered, dread and a strange excitement knotting her stomach.

"You, you stubborn, headstrong woman. You and your old fears. And I'm going to win. Now lock your van and let's go. The plane's fueled and ready."

"And if I refuse?"

"Don't bother." Catching her wrist in a steel grasp, he pulled her from the car and onto the skillet-hot surface of the runway. Heat mirages danced in the distance, wavering across the asphalt desert.

Carly spotted a lone figure, a mechanic judging from his overalls, working near a single engine plane a short distance away. "Hello there," she yelled. "Help!" She feigned a struggle, trying to get his attention.

The mechanic lifted one hand, shielding his eyes from the sun's glare. "Watcha say?"

In one smooth, fluid motion, Matt hoisted Carly onto the top step of the plane and propelled her into the cabin. "It's okay," he shouted, waving and laughing. "I'm kidnapping her for the weekend." He locked the door behind him.

The mechanic, wiping the sweat from his brow with the sleeves of his shirt, muttered, "Hmmmph. People are sure into kinky things nowadays."

Matt buckled first a silent, glowering Carly and then himself into the cockpit seats, ran a quick check of the instrument panel, and started the engine. In moments the plane lifted like a sleek, silver gull over the shining waters of Lake Michigan.

Minute after minute, Carly stared angrily out the window at the rush and sweep of cloud and water below. Her heart fluttered in her throat. Her head spun. She heard Matt talking to the control tower far below, felt the plane level out at the desired altitude, its speed becoming almost imperceptible now. A sideways glance caught Matt grinning at her, and Carly glared back out the window.

He reached across and lay a warm hand just above her knee. Carly brushed it off. He put it back again, higher this time, his fingers curving around her thigh. When she moved to push his hand away, his fingers tightened, edging ever so slightly upward the tempting V of her jeans. A river of sensation flooded her in melting heat. She sat still, totally aware of his touch, his unnerving grin, the piercing gaze of his blue eyes, trying to feign indifference.

"So Sting knows how to fly a plane. I thought his forte was the *land* speed record."

"He's a versatile guy."

"Don't tell me NASA provided our transportation today?"

"Nope. A friend in Chicago. Said he could spare it for a few days. For a good cause." He gave her a look that made her knees tremble against the seat.

"Well, I hope he's not too disappointed when he

finds out what a waste it was!" She knocked his hand away and quickly turned her back to him.

"Gypsy, the only thing that's going to be wasted is the energy you're wasting on being angry with me."

The sure arrogance of his tone infuriated her. Spinning back to face him, she fumed, "If you think I'm going to talk to you, or listen to one word you have to say, Matt Linton, you have another thought coming! I'm not some starry-eyed teenager who thinks it's romantic to be dragged off by her hair! I have a business. Responsibilities . . . oh!" she groaned suddenly, burying her face in her hands. "Oh, my business! The lecture! . . ."

"It's all right. I called Maria."

"You what?"

"Yup. This time you had really left. And"—he winked—"she thought it was a good idea. So the business is safe."

"You what? She . . . she what? And the university . . ."

"You guessed it! Even the most respected guest lecturer is sometimes called suddenly out of town. They understood."

"They . . . they . . . oh, you scoundrel! You . . . you presumptuous man!"

"It's called desperate."

"It's called crazy! Oh, I'd like to have you locked up for the rest of your natural . . . or *unnatural* . . . life, Matt Linton!"

139

"Only if you're my jailor, Carly West." Something flickered in his eyes that made her heart leap to her throat.

Speechless, she turned back to the floating panorama below.

Almost an hour later her heart took another unexpected leap. "That's . . . that's the upper peninsula." Her dark eyes were wide with disbelief. "We've crossed state lines. *Two* state lines! I . . . I'll invoke the Lindbergh Law, the Mann Act . . . the—"

"Hang on! We're coming in for a landing." He snapped on the radio. "Marquette, this is . . ."

The elegant little jet skimmed the runway, then touched down light as a feather.

Matt flung open the door and helped Carly out. "Perfect. And there's a little jeep waiting to take us to the cabin." He pointed across the field. "Want to help me with the luggage?"

His low, husky laughter curled around her as she stalked to the jeep. He appeared moments later lugging a suitcase with a carton full of supplies balanced against one lean hip. Reaching under the car seat, he retrieved the waiting keys and flashed Carly a victorious smile. Then the jeep headed east.

Despite herself, Carly was intrigued by the mystery, her senses sharp and finely tuned to each passing moment. And her emotions never lost touch with the man who was charging the moments with electricity and magic. What had happened to her perfect self-control? And what had happened to that easy, calm professor whose look and touch now suddenly commanded her heart? The physical tension thrummed between them in the narrow confines of the jeep, more palpable than the heat of the sun or the wash of the wind against her face.

Frantic to hide her emotions, Carly focused her attention on the winding road ahead. The lake rolled heavily against the shore to the right, while dark stands of scrub and pine edged the opposite shoulder. She had been to the upper peninsula before, had even flown into the Marquette airport, but today it all looked different. Wilder. Subtly charged with danger and excitement. Or was it the man beside her who shifted the focus of her world?

"What are you thinking about?"

"Nothing you'd want to hear, believe me! I happen to be furious with you, Professor!"

"Don't be. I'm such a nice guy. And I have it on the best authority that I'm quite a sexy fellow." His smile had a trace of boyishness that always snatched her breath away.

"Don't believe everything you hear, Professor!" The echo of her own words had made her cheeks burn.

"Well, maybe we can take a survey later."

"I wouldn't set my heart on it if I were you."

"Sorry. My heart's always beyond my control." He settled an arm around her shoulder but she was quick to shrug it off. He only grinned. Time was on

141

his side. And circumstance. Definitely circumstance.

The cabin was half hidden in the woods, set on a small rise above the lakeshore. Matt pulled up close to the railed porch, hefted the suitcase and the supplies up on the wooden floor, and began taking things inside.

"Coming?"

"No," Carly snapped.

"Okay. Fine." He shrugged. "But be sure to watch out for bears. Wolves. An occasional coyote. And some damned big badgers up on vacation from Wisconsin." The words punctuated each step. Pausing to open the screen door with two free fingers and the curve of his shoulder, he tossed a final beckoning smile her way and stepped inside.

Carly sat stubbornly in the jeep while a cool breeze off the lake lifted the hair on her neck and soothed the angry heat of her blood. She saw the calico curtains blow in the screened windows of the neat wooden house. She saw the dark silhouette of Matt's body through the open door and heard the rich, pleasant tones of his voice as he hummed to himself from within.

What right did he have to be so content? The cat that swallowed the canary—that's what he was purring like! Carly tried to stoke her anger but somehow, unexplainably, the fire was dying out. And in its place was the familiar heat of her longing and the rising flame of her love.

142

But she was damned if she was going to let Matt Linton know it!

Hopping from the jeep, she stepped inside.

"So . . . this is your hideaway. Hmmmm. Do you have places like this scattered across the country to satisfy Sting's appetite for lascivious escapades?"

"Nope." He stopped to watch her, one thick brow cocked questioningly above his shining blue eyes. "No, this is the only one. Only for now. Only for you. Dave, my son, helped arrange it."

"Dave?" Carly's brows shot up in surprise. "That's a surprise. He seems a most unlikely accomplice."

"Perhaps. Perhaps not. I thought about a lot of things these few days without you, Carly. Realized a lot of things. And you were right about Dave and me. The past is done and we've got to make the future work between us. My daughter, Tracy, too. Jenna seems to have her hands full with her as well."

Carly lowered her head for a moment. "I'm glad you're working it out together, Matt. Really I am."

"Well, you helped make me see some things, Carly. And for that I thank you." He touched her lightly on the shoulder.

Carly immediately flung up her defenses. "All it proves, sir, is that you haven't completely taken leave of your senses yet!" She slipped from beneath his hand and turned away.

"Oh, yes I have," Matt murmured softly but Carly chose to ignore his words.

"So. Just how long do you intend on holding me prisoner here?"

"Hope to make it out before the first snow," he answered. "In the meantime I'm going to woo you with good food and wine. Want to help me cook?"

The thought of rubbing elbows in the cozy little galley kitchen she spotted out of the corner of her eye was terribly enticing but Carly banished the traitorous idea from her brain. "Are you kidding!" she huffed. "I wouldn't eat a morsel you prepared. *Or* drink a sip of your wine. I'm going out to scout the area. Maybe I can find some friendly neighbor who'll drive me back to civilization."

"Nearest neighbor's a good ten miles away. I checked. Have fun." Matt choked back his amusement and tied an apron around his waist.

Carly watched the apron pull tightly around his hips and felt his eyes pull her toward him. She could feel the rush of heat collect within her and begin to spread. Hurriedly she spun around and bolted through the cabin door.

As she reached the bottom of the slope, she slowed her steps. Was he following her? Would he come racing down the hill, catch her in his arms, and make mad passionate love to her there under the blue dome of the sky? Heart pounding, she glanced over her shoulder. Her dark eyes widened in disappointment; there wasn't a sign of him.

"Well, he'd better not try it," she grumbled aloud to the scurrying chipmunks and tiny tree toads. And she trudged on alone into the blue-black shadows of the pines.

As always, the stillness of the woods calmed her, draining away the tension through the bottom of her feet and into the loamy earth below. She swung her arms, tossed her hair, and smiled. What an interesting day this had turned out to be!

Stepping lightly on the carpet of pine needles and moss, scuffing her toes into the tumbled heaps of pinecones, Carly walked on through the woods. She knelt to peer at the rubbery, lobster-red roof of a mushroom that was steadily pushing its way free of the earth. Talk about stubborn! She gathered a handful of lavender asters and marveled at the perfection of each petal. Halted nose-to-nose with a black-eyed, tail-twitching chipmunk perched on a low branch, its mouth clamped possessively around an acorn half its size.

"It's okay," she whispered, and it whisked its tail and vanished, a tiny, chattering magician. The acorn rolled to her feet. She bent and picked it up, then dropped it for luck into her pocket.

By the time Carly had circled past the lake and back up to the cabin, her pockets were laden with pebbles, a gull's ragged feather, and a handful of berries. Topping the rise from behind, she was met by a welcoming curl of smoke from the chimney and the silver-toned strummings of a classical guitar. Matt sat on an old weathered bench beside the back door, one leg balanced on a boulder and his body bent gracefully over the polished instrument.

She stopped to watch him, her own presence undetected. He leaned over the guitar as over a lover and she saw the same gentle intensity in the curve of his arms, the same tenderness that guided the touch of his fingers. She had known that gentleness, that sweetness. Yearned beyond all sense and reason to know it again. Even if it were for just one more day. Stepping into his line of vision, she whispered, "Well, hello, Segovia."

His head snapped up and a welcoming smile lit his face. "Hi! I didn't hear you come up. Glad you're back." His sky-blue gaze warmed her face.

"Music soothes the savage beast—or so they say." She hesitated, her voice unsure. "I didn't know you played classical guitar. It was lovely."

"Thank you. But I told you. That's why I brought you here. So you could get to know me. All of me, for better or for worse."

"Kidnapped me," she corrected automatically, and the thought made her reach for the easy security of her anger. "Look at that—you brought a guitar, and I don't even have a toothbrush!"

"*I* had time to pack."

"Premeditated! I thought so! You know what the courts will say about that! Just when did you begin planning this little adventure?"

"Last night. After the fortieth unanswered phone

call. When I was lying alone and lonely in my bed. But I did call to invite you."

"You did? When?"

"When you told Maria to tell me you weren't there." He smiled at her blush and continued. "So I was driven to desperate measures. But, to alleviate your fears—you *can* share my toothbrush."

"How very generous of you!"

Straightening from his position on the bench, Matt moved closer. "Give me a chance, Gypsy. I want to be even nicer."

Her blood raced like fire through her veins. Why couldn't she control the effect he had on her? Why did she love him so?

Misreading her silence, he backed away a step. "It's all right. I only meant at dinner. At least for now. Come on in." Holding the guitar loosely in one hand, he pushed the door wide for her. "It's beef bourguignon with fresh green beans, hot rolls. And Cabernet Sauvignon."

"Ah, a wonderfully rustic meal. Thanks anyway but I think I'll have an apple."

"Suit yourself." Placing the guitar on a shelf, he lit the two candles on the already set table, sat down, and poured himself a glass of wine.

Carly grabbed an apple from the refrigerator. She perched on a stool in the corner of the kitchen and chomped noisily on the cold fruit. "Great apple!" She drew no response. Matt ate quietly, sipping his wine and buttering his hot rolls.

"Oh, forget it!" Carly muttered, tossed the apple into the trash, and raced to the table.

"I'm starving. And you know it! Shoot—let it be said I sold out for beef bourguignon!"

Matt grinned and glanced at his watch. "Right on time. I figured you'd last about three minutes—"

Carly wanted to retort but couldn't. Her mouth was busy closing around her first bite of the warm flaky crust of the roll.

It was a wonderful dinner, and between the delicate tastes, the heady potency of the wine, and Matt's nearness, Carly felt herself growing dizzy and weakening, softening. She had a sudden image of herself as a bonbon—its sweet, sticky hidden center melting and flowing across the table to land right in his lap. The thought made her smile and then almost laugh out loud. Her cheeks burned at the mental image.

Matt eyed her quizzically. Then his gaze narrowed and darkened with arousal. He caught her hand and drew her toward him, pulling her from her chair and into his arms.

Carly slipped away, the laughter dying in her throat. "Oh, no, Professor. Please don't let Sting take advantage of my somewhat unsteady condition. I'm . . . I'm suddenly very sleepy. Good night. I'm going to bed." She looked around, her eyes wide and unseeing. "Where *is* bed?"

"Right here in my arms," he growled. Threading his fingers through hers, he pulled her close again.

She felt the heat of his body stir and awaken a thousand secret emotions within her. She could not trust herself to be near him. "No . . . no," she stuttered. "Bed. Single bed. *My* bed."

"Oh, *that* bed," he laughed seductively, his hands sliding over her shoulders and down toward her high firm breasts in slow, sensual exploration. "That would be a waste, my darling."

"Stop! Halt—whoa." Trembling, she broke free of his hungry embrace and mustered the ragged remains of her injured dignity. "I couldn't consider surrendering to a kidnapper, Mr. Linton . . . and if you're any kind of a gentleman, you'll kindly point me to my bed."

He leaned closer. His eyes blazed at her with an all-consuming passion but a whisper of a smile still tugged at his lips. "Up there." He pointed behind her, his gaze never faltering from her face. His voice was a breath on her lips. "And if you really, *really* expect to get in there alone, you had better get going now—fast!"

She spun and bolted for the loft ladder without a backward glance. From her safe roost a story up, she finally turned back to look at him. Desire drew a pointed finger up her spine, sending ripples of excitement circling over her flesh. "Don't you dare set foot on this ladder, Matt Linton," she whispered shakily.

"Not without an invitation, Gypsy," he drawled softly. Stepping closer, he stopped directly beneath

149

her and looked up, his face expressionless except for the steady flame in his blue eyes.

Like a moth drawn irresistibly to the flame, her feet were drawn back to the ladder. But catching herself, she turned and vanished into the secure shadows of the loft.

The night had grown surprisingly chilly. Or was it the lonely distance between them, Carly wondered. At first she could hear Matt moving around below, and the solid comfort of his step, the crackle and pop of a log as he set the fire in the hearth, the creak of the springs in the old sofa. Then it grew still and the night silence drew her into its depths. She pulled the loose folds of Matt's red flannel shirt closer around her breasts and tugged it down over her bottom. Every restless turn hiked it back up again. Wrapping the thin blanket tightly about her, she tried to burrow into the curve of the old metal bed.

She did not know when she dozed, or what woke her. Only that she was colder than before, and even lonelier for the nearness of him.

Stealing to the edge of the ladder, she peered down. The fire cast a fitful light across the rough-hewn walls but left much of the room in shadow. "Matt?" she whispered and strained to hear his answer. There wasn't any. "Matt?" she called again and set one bare foot on the top rung. She could feel the night's chill across her instep, and a shiver ran up her arm.

Where was he? Where had he gone? The ghosts of old childhood fears fluttered around her heart. Don't be a silly goose, she scolded silently. But her stomach wasn't listening; it continued to do acrobatics.

Without further thought, she skittered down the remaining rungs of the ladder, the tails of the red flannel shirt flapping around the tops of her thighs. She dashed to the hearth and its beckoning warmth.

It was then she nearly tripped over Matt. He was lying on the floor just at the boundary of the fire's warmth, his long frame wrapped in a pile of quilts, one bare arm thrown across the top. He looked so damned peaceful, so contented, it made her grit her teeth. She wanted to punch him. How dare he bring her out here against her will, stir up a thousand unmanageable emotions—then sleep like a baby? The man had no conscience. No sense of guilt! He treated the whole thing like some wild adventure, like the prelude to some fantastic crescendo, or the appetizer before dessert! And guess who was the cherries jubilee!

Narrowing her eyes, Carly bent over, rested her hands on her knees, and took a good long look. The firelight played magically over his face, highlighting the brows that curved like fuzzy caterpillars over his closed eyes. How remarkable were the dark lashes that lay against his cheeks. Such a nice nose. And that finely chiseled mouth that seemed even in sleep to tug at the corners in wry amusement. Why, oh why, did he have to be so good to look at, so wonderful to touch? At the thought, her fingertips remembered the feel of his warm skin. She touched him lightly, just once on the muscled curve of shoulder that rose above the blankets. Then she tore her hand away. How could she ever live without the feel and sight of him?

Tears welled in her eyes and she banished them with anger. Why couldn't he have left well enough alone and just vanished from her life? Now what was she going to do? "Damn you, Matt Linton!" she whispered thickly. "How can you sleep when I'm so miserable and confused and cold?"

As if on cue, a chilling draft swept across the floor and up her bare slender legs. Her skin shivered into goose bumps. There were only two sources of heat in the room. The fire . . . and Matt. For just a moment, Carly let herself dream of lifting the quilts and sliding in beside his warm, enticing body, and lying there, sandwiched by the heat, until she'd grow drowsy in his arms.

Her cold toes brought her back to reality. "The least you can do, Matt Linton, is share those blankets," she muttered.

Reaching down, she caught hold of one edge of the top quilt and pulled. It slid a little way across his body, then snagged under his arm. She tugged again. It was definitely stuck. It wouldn't budge. Gathering a handful of blankets in her fists, she shifted her weight and gave one good hard yank. At that moment, Matt raised his arm.

Carly tumbled back into the sofa. The blankets swirled around her feet. And Matt Linton lay stark naked on the floor.

Carly gasped, her hand flying to her lips, her eyes round as saucers.

Matt lazily opened one eye and grinned. "Well, hi there. If this is what you wanted, Gypsy, you only had to ask."

"No, Matt . . . I . . ."

"Go on, darlin'. Let's hear you talk yourself out of this one." His eyes sparkled. Without the slightest trace of self-consciousness he folded both arms behind his head and smiled up at her. The fire was doing lovely things to his long, lean body, tracing the planes and hollows of his form with dancing light. She struggled to pull her eyes away, but failed. He was so exciting to look at, this man, this wonderful male body that so complemented and completed her own. Their brief intimacy had only intensified the mystery. She knew what he could do to her. But not why or how.

Matt saw the torment in her eyes and his own desire flamed to fever pitch. Fire swirled in his loins. Every fiber of his being yearned to wipe away her confusion and fill her with the surety of his passion and love. It took all his constraint to keep from ravishing her. He couldn't push. Must be patient.

Forcing an easy smile, he teased softly, ". . . wish I had known . . ."

Her dark eyes slid to where the uncontrollable stirrings of his body belied his easy words. Heat suffused her pale cheeks. "You . . . you don't look very worried, Professor."

"But I am. Worried you wouldn't believe how much I love you. How much I want you."

"Oh," Carly breathed deeply. "I . . . I *do* believe you. I just don't know what to do about it."

Laughing deep in his throat, Matt brought his arm forward, circling it around her knees, and tumbled her down on top of him. "I've got the answer to that one, Carly. Trust me . . ."

The welcoming heat of his body seared the doubts away. Matching laughter bubbled in her throat. There was no pleasure on earth or in heaven as exquisite as the meshing of their bodies, inch to inch, the threading of their souls together.

She wrapped her arms around him, pressing her slender, fiercely responding body against his. Her fingers were woven in the rough curls of his hair, his in the dark smoky cloud of hers. Their lips met in a fierce, urgent kiss, then parted and met again, mouths hungry for the sweet satisfying taste of each other.

"Matt," she murmured against his lips. "How do you do this to me? This is not what I'd planned. . . ." Her brain was foggy with desire. It registered only the feel of his body against her, the scent of

154

him, the taste. She saw him bared in the lapping firelight, agleam with the light sweat of arousal, and he was more beautiful than any fantasy . . . yet this could *not* be real—

"This . . . this won't work . . ." She struggled to make sense of her words.

"It's worked for centuries, my darling Carly. Just watch." Matt slid his hands up over the round firm flesh of her buttocks and under the red flannel shirt. With deft swiftness he slipped it off her unresisting body and gathered her nakedness against him.

She circled her arms around his neck, her body moving slowly with a sweet, seductive rhythm, her thighs bare against his and her aching breasts caressing his chest.

Matt shuddered, feeling his body flooded with unleashed passion. With trembling hands he stroked the smooth curves of her back, cupped her buttocks, and urged her higher against him. "I love you, Carly. Don't be frightened, darling. I'd never hurt you."

The yielding softness of her body invited his hardness, demanded it. He moaned, his chest rising and falling heavily beneath the sweet burden of her weight. His hands slipped between them, stroking her, playing across her taut belly and lower until his fingers tangled in her curls and soft high cries gathered in her throat.

"Let it go, Carly," he urged, his own voice husked with fierce emotion. "Let it go. I'll catch you."

"Come with me," she begged, digging her fingers into the muscular padding of his shoulders and chest. Arching away ever so slightly, she drew her lips down over his throat and chest, parted her lips, and touched her tongue to his hard nipples.

He groaned and she swirled the hot searing wetness of her tongue across his nipples again and again until he writhed beneath her.

Pulling his hands free, he captured her hips and shifted their weight until she half lay, half sat astride him.

A spark of wild delight flashed in Carly's dark, gypsy eyes. Leaning farther back, she pulled her knees up along his hips, one on either side, and drew herself slowly back and forth across him. "Matt . . . oh, Matt . . ." Her body flamed and spun in tantalizing waves of arousal.

"Oh, Carly, what are you doing to me?" he groaned. "I'm on fire. Touch me!"

Carly needed no coaxing. Her eyes feasted on the surfeit of emotions that transformed his face. Emotions mirroring her own. Love, excitement, pleasure so great it bordered on pain.

Again his hands began their magic strumming across the fine tight wires of her senses. He caressed her everywhere, touching her with breath-catching intimacy that seemed so right. Sparks flew and danced across her body, making her cry out with a need as fierce as his wanting.

He whispered her name and slid deep within her.

His hardness and strength and love filled her, consuming her. They moved together, their bodies learning and relearning the uncharted realms, the inner lands that can be explored only by two. Two merging into one. Melting, fusing, loving. Matt's breathing and pulse and rhythm matching her own, guiding and lifting Carly until the fire dimmed and the cabin fell away. And all that was left was the heart of each exploding together in a crucible of flame.

For an instant the world rocked, then settled back on its axis.

And Matt and Carly floated earthward on the wings of the purest, profoundest peace.

CHAPTER EIGHT

Somewhere in the distance birds warbled and sang and rode the lift of the crisp wind through tall waving pines. A new sun arose unseen and settled over the labyrinth of lakes, coating the rippled waters a golden hue. Animals of the woods—gophers and small fox and deer on silent feet—emerged from the dewy dawn to forage for their breakfast near the small cabin, its only sign of life a feathery wisp of smoke rising from the chimney.

And Carly West felt the drift of that world filter in through the small open crack in the window and instinctively nestled down deeper beneath the bundle of blankets, pressing her body into the warm one sleeping next to her.

"M-m-m-m," he responded sleepily. "There's a bear in my bed. . . ."

"Bare what?" Carly playfully nuzzled the soft skin at the base of Matt's neck and ran one hand slowly over the rise of firm hips and the smoothness of his abdomen. Beneath his skin she could feel the quick intake of breath, the instant change from the slow, gentle breathing of sleep to the rapid beginnings of arousal.

"Listen, Lady-in-my-bed," Matt growled, "from now on you're going to have to take full responsibility for your actions. And remember—there's no one within miles to calm this savage beast you're unleashing in me."

Carly smiled as she watched those great deep eyes shed the haze of sleep, then slowly turn and register on her own face. He drew one hand from beneath the downy comforter and cupped her chin as he gazed into her eyes.

"Well, Gypsy?"

"The beast is really a pussy cat. I'm not afraid of—"

Her purring voice was swallowed by his lips and mouth as he drew her to him and wrapped her in an embrace as fierce and rich as the passion that swelled between them. It was a long, sweet kiss, one that passed through Carly's whole body, awakening her fully to every slight-pressured touch of him, every point where their bodies touched beneath the mountain of feathers and cloth.

"Every day should begin like this. Each dawn.

Each sunrise," Matt murmured into the soft feathery waves of her hair.

"Is it day then? I hardly knew, nor what day it is—"

Matt chuckled huskily. "Friday, I *think*—"

"Friday's child is loving and giving," Carly crooned softly. *Friday.* The day registered slowly beyond the peaceful world of their lovemaking, beyond the confines of the isolated cabin. "Friday? *Friday!*" Carly jerked forward with such suddenness she lost the warm cocoon of quilts. "Friday . . . oh, heavens no!" Her eyes were wide and clear now as she bolted upright on the floor, the cold lake air circling her naked body and causing tiny bumps to rise along her arms. "Matt, the auditors are coming!"

Matt watched her with uncomprehending amusement and a teasing smile curved his lips. "It's okay, Carly. I'd say our figures are just fine—" He reached up and traced a finger down the firm curve of her breast. Then tried to draw her back into the nesting warmth of the blankets.

"No!" She resisted his gentle tug. "I mean it, Matt. The auditors are coming today. To the store. I have to be there!"

She struggled out of the jumble of covers and wrapped a sheet around her shivering body. "I'm sorry, Matt. I was in such a tizzy yesterday, I didn't even think—But I truly do have to get back. And *you* have to take me. Now!" Leaning over, she grabbed a corner of the blanket pile and with a mighty jerk pulled them into a heap beside him.

She stood for a moment, looking down at the long length of Matt, lying naked in the cold northern air, his eyes hooded and his body relaxed beneath her scrutiny.

"I can't deny it," she said, her gaze traveling over the unhidden beauty of him. Her eyes smoldered, caressing him with sweet desire. "You *are* tempting!"

Matt winked and beckoned with one hand. "Come back . . . just for a moment—"

"Nope. Sorry, fella. Up! You have just enough time while I shower to fix us each a cup of coffee." With great difficulty, she pulled her eyes away and headed for the loft.

Matt leaned against the doorframe of the tiny office behind the kite store and followed Carly's frantic movements with maddening calm. Papers flew wildly as she sought to ready herself for the auditor's arrival.

"Matt, please. Just go. You returned me safe and sound—and I'll recommend you highly to anyone contemplating being kidnapped. But now you need to leave so I can get this done. We're home. It's the real world now . . . and I'm no longer under your power!"

There was an edge to her voice, fueled by Matt's stubborn insistence on discussing their relationship

—"no holds barred," as he so irritatingly put it—now! "Listen, Matt—maybe we can have coffee tomorrow at the university and talk—"

Matt tried again, his voice registering his weariness from the battle that had begun fifty thousand feet up, somewhere between Marquette, Michigan, and Chicago. "Carly, we have to talk now. We can't just let this thing slip away from us. We left a lot of things unfinished, unsaid. I took you up there to *settle* some things, not to make it even more complicated. I wanted us both to face up to things and I'm not going to let a damn-fool audit foil those plans!"

Suddenly he felt tired and raw. Raw with need, raw with emotion, raw with love for the ebony-eyed gypsy who could even now try to walk out of his life.

"This is not the time, Matt. Surely you can see that!" Angrily she pulled a ledger off the shelf and threw it on the table. "And I don't know if there *is* anything to settle. Kidnapping doesn't really solve problems, you know—"

"Carly . . . ?"

"Okay," she amended softly, a half-smile curving her lips. "It was . . . quite fantastic. Being with you like that. But, Matt—" She turned and looked at him long and level. "Matt, you're gentle, tender—an incredible lover. I admit all that. And I admit that I care a lot about you! But I . . . I still have a lot of things to work through. Like the fact that getting really close to another person and coming to depend on him frightens me." She stumbled over

162

the tears that threatened to choke her. "Like the fact that we're two such very different people! You're stubborn and single-minded and—"

"Carly, listen to yourself! You could be describing *either* of us."

"No! You're wrong. We're *very* different, take my word for it!" The tears spilled down her face and she mopped at them clumsily with the back of her hand, her shoulders shaking with sobs.

It tore Matt apart to see her cry like that. His touch was as soft as cotton wool, yet sent shivers flying through Carly's arm and she jerked away. "No, Matt!"

"Carly, at least be honest with me. I love you. In a very special way, a way that has touched every blasted part of my being. And a love like that is rare. It carries with it a special—"

"My father and mother loved each other once. But that love couldn't overcome their differences or prevent them from fighting. And my friend Beth, she loved, too. In that same crazy, passionate, blinding way. I watched her fall in love . . . and thrive on love . . . and then almost die from it!" Her voice lowered as she tried to calm the emotion. "She thought—honestly thought—that her love was very special. That it could carry them through anything together. Forever. And *you*, Matt, you and Jenna . . .

"Matt, I love you too much to ever hurt you. But I'm also afraid of being hurt." She forced a smile on

163

her pale face and a lightness into her voice. "Maybe . . . maybe I'm just too selfish. Maybe we should just finish up the summer with a wild, glorious summer love affair, with enough heat and passion to warm us through the long, cold winter. And then *maybe* next summer, *maybe* you'll come back and . . . and should circumstances allow, *maybe* we could—"

"Carly, stop it! This is not some three-month love affair we're talking about. I'm talking forever!"

Carly silently fingered the papers in her hand and stared at the jumble of typed numbers running together in a blur.

"Forever, Carly West! I want you in my life permanently."

The papers were now a tangled mess in Carly's hands. She released her tight-knuckled grip and watched them float to the floor and settle in an oddly flat patch of sunlight. Slowly she lifted her eyes to Matt's. "Matt, my head's spinning right now. There's so much I don't know about you . . . and about myself. I can't seem to sort things out—and I'm so afraid . . ."

"Then just listen with your heart for a minute, Carly. Let it help you understand, help you face up to things.

"You told me after my son was here that *I* was afraid of my feelings. I thought about it long and hard, and I realized you were right; I *was* afraid, damned afraid of hurting *you*. I've seen people hurt by love, too, and *I've* done some of the hurting. David was a reminder of all that. But I've learned from my mistakes, Carly." He smiled softly. "I'll never hurt you."

Needing just the touch of her, he let his hand fall lightly on her shoulder. "I can't explain about your parents. Or Beth. But I do know life demands some risks, and I thought *you* were willing to take them. If the star was bright enough, I thought you'd be the one to soar to it. You have some thinking to do, too, Carly. Only fair, right?" He smiled gently into her face, filled now with her huge ebony eyes and the thick fringe of lashes that swept across her flushed cheeks.

The jangle of the telephone was a blessing, an unexpected reprieve that broke the tension into tiny manageable pieces.

Carly moved like a sleepwalker and lifted the receiver slowly. Her voice was soft and controlled. "Affairs of the Air. May I help you?" There was a long pause while Carly listened to the voice on the other end of the phone line. Matt watched her face with a curious alarm. Her expression seemed tighter, her high cheekbones shadowing the rest of her narrow face. She kept her eyes lowered, shielded tightly from Matt's keen, probing gaze.

"I see—" Carly's fingers twisted tightly around the smooth white receiver. "Yes . . . yes, he's here. Of course you may speak to him."

She covered the voice piece with her hand as she

held the phone out to Matt. "It's for you, Professor Linton. Your wife would like to speak to you."

Matt stared at her for a moment, first alarmed at the coolness in her voice, then irritated by the look of infuriating self-righteousness that swept over her face. He took the phone roughly, muttered "ex-wife" tersely to Carly, then spoke to Jenna in cool, friendly tones.

Carly quickly slipped out into the tiny hallway and closed the door softly behind her. She leaned against the cool outer wall, forcing deep breaths of air into her lungs. Through the door leading into the store came muffled sounds of kites being bought and sold and admired, the constant tinkling of the silver bells tied to the front door. But today the sounds were flat and joyless when they reached Carly's ears and she wished only for a silence that wasn't there.

"Carly—" Matt stood framed in the opposite doorway, his long handsome face drawn with conflicting emotions. "I have to go to California. Right away. My daughter, Tracy, unexpectedly dropped out of school and decided to get married. Tomorrow. Jenna couldn't reach me sooner."

Carly stared at him for a moment, then shifted her gaze to an imaginary spot on the floor. No, of course she couldn't reach him. He had been busy kidnapping *her*. And then . . . then they had been "busy" with one another. Now he must feel awful, not having been there when his family needed him.

Matt continued, "Jenna is busy picking up the pieces and trying to plan some semblance of a wedding. A church and all that—" He paused. "We'd both want that; she's our only daughter, you know."

Carly raised her eyes to his. "I understand. Of course you need to be there. Is there anything I can do to help you?"

"Yes."

Carly was stilled by the husky plea in his voice. "Come with me." His eyes looked deep into hers. "I need you there with me, Carly."

"Matt, I . . ." Carly brushed away the hot wetness on her cheeks with the back of her hand. Her throat ached with tightness and she found it difficult to speak. "Matt—I can't go with you. You know that. I can barely deal with the present now. I can't go back into your past."

"I *need* you, Carly. You're a part of my life now, whether you're ready to admit that or not. And that includes the past as well as the future."

He watched her for a long time, his eyes pleading with her, his face raw and vulnerable. His words hung like a fragile hammock between them.

Carly felt empty, hollow. If she accompanied him to California, she would be making a commitment to him, and she just didn't feel ready to do that. An overwhelming sadness washed over her as she turned her eyes to his. "No, Matt. I can't. I won't go with you."

Without another word, Matt turned slowly and

walked straight ahead. He moved through the kite store, out into the sunshine—and out of Carly West's life.

Beth Lewis found Carly exactly where she had said she'd be—folded into the back booth at Casey's Bar, sipping a tasteless margarita that had not yet begun to numb the pain.

"Carly—" Beth slipped down across from Carly and clasped her friend's hands in her own. "Carly, what's happened?" She probed Carly's swollen eyes in the dim light of the shadowed booth and saw the pain that settled there.

"Oh, Carly. I see. It's Matt Linton, isn't it?"

Carly sniffed and fumbled for another tissue in her purse. "Yes, Beth. Damn! It's Matt Linton. I . . . I want him so much right now I feel as if I'm going to die. I want to hear him laugh, to touch him. Just to *look* at him, to be close to him. My life is torn to pieces, Beth, and I . . . I don't know how to patch it. It's divided into Matt and before-Matt. Matt . . . and without Matt. And there's no way I can figure out how to live without him. You've got to help me—"

"You love him very much." It wasn't a question. Simply an acknowledgment of the emotions on Carly's face, the tone of her voice, the soft warmth in her eyes beneath the tears.

"And it hurts like hell!"

Carly stared blindly at the smudged circles her

fingers had made where they idled on the Formica tabletop. She lifted her hand and ran long fingers through the tangled mass of waves that engulfed her face. "I need you to help me, Beth. To help me disentangle myself from him . . . emotionally, I mean."

"Why?"

"Why?" Carly was taken aback, and strangely hurt at Beth's question. The "why's" were so obvious, so shatteringly clear.

"Beth, I love him. But I'm afraid to live my life being so dependent on one person. What if our feelings for each other change? What if we end up fighting and arguing the way my parents did? I can't risk having my life torn apart."

"Carly—" Beth's voice was gentle and she bent her blond head toward Carly as she spoke. "Carly, stop it for a moment. You said yourself you're feeling torn now. Do you really love him?"

"Yes, Beth. There's no doubt of that. But I know what love can turn into. I've seen what can happen over the years. . . ."

"Listen, Carly, don't you know that what you're doing is wrong?"

"No, Beth, *you* listen. What right have I to think our love—Matt's and mine—is any different from anyone else's? Why should our love be impervious to the same problems that eroded yours and Jack's? *Or* my parents'?" Her eyes lit on the pained expres-

169

sion on Beth's face and she stopped. "I'm sorry, Beth, I didn't mean—"

"You should be *sorry*, Carly West! Sorry that you're being such a fool. That you're painting your life with colors from someone else's palette!"

Her voice rose and several bystanders turned curious eyes toward the two young women huddled in the corner booth. Beth blushed and continued in slightly more subdued tones.

"You have every right in the world to think your love for Matt is special and different. Because it *is!* Because it's *yours*. And mine will be, too, when I find it. And you can be damned sure I'm going to keep looking until I do!"

The intensity and determination in Beth's soft voice caused Carly to smile.

"But, Carly"—Beth's breath flickered the flame above the stubby candle in the center of the table— "if you've found him, there's nothing left to look for, is there?"

They sat in silence then, letting the cool tequila slide down their throats and ward off the evening chill. Each was lost in thought and wrapped in emotion.

"Carly?" Beth broke the silence hesitatingly.

"Yes, Beth . . ." The vagueness had disappeared from Carly's eyes and she smiled at Beth softly.

"Carly, maybe you need to stop thinking about what will happen if you live with him—and visualize what your life will be like without him."

A long, knowing look passed between the two friends.

Carly groped for her last tissue and blew her nose with finality. She rose from the padded bench and dropped several bills on the table.

"Where are you going?" Beth leaned back and watched her friend, a concerned look on her face.

"For a walk. I need to do some thinking." Carly leaned over and kissed Beth lightly on the cheek. "Thank you," she said and disappeared out into the night.

CHAPTER NINE

Carly peered over the cab driver's shoulder into the cracked mirror and straightened her hat.

"Lady, you look terrific. They'll love ya!" he growled as only cabbies can.

"But is it all right? For a wedding, I mean—"

The balding driver glanced sideways and eyed her shaking hands. "You the bride?"

"Oh, no!" Carly gasped, then laughed and eyed herself in the mirror. "But the hat . . . Do people out here wear hats to weddings?"

"Absolutely! I never go without one. You the bridesmaid?"

Carly smoothed a wayward strand of shiny dark hair beneath the wide brim of her linen hat, its deep-rose band matching the glow in her cheeks. "Oh, no!"

"Ah, I got it. Bride's best friend from some fancy school—"

"No. We've never met." She edged up in the seat again to view the scalloped neckline of the soft full blouse curving over her breasts.

The cabbie scowled. "So where ya from, lady?"

"Chicago. The Windy City." Carly laughed nervously.

Chicago . . . it seemed so far behind her. Millions of miles away. She had left that morning on the first available flight and had not arrived at the San Francisco airport until 11 A.M. She had dialed Matt's number, and found his message waiting for her.

Carly, if by heaven's grace you come, we're at Holy Angel's Church, 212 West Ocean Avenue. Wedding is at noon. I love you.

Such few words, but in his voice they meant everything.

And now she was racing to him, her nerves jangled, her stomach lurching with each careless curve of the cab.

"You come from Chicago to go to a wedding of a dame you never met . . . and you're shakin' like a leaf. Lady, you sure got me confused! What the heck are you going to this wedding for?"

Carly shook her head, her dark eyes huge in her pale oval face. "To find me a man!"

She opened the window a crack and let the salty ocean air circle in and calm her down.

She hadn't slept much the night before, of that she was fairly sure. But everything else was a blur. Beth had dropped her at the airport at nine, hugged her fiercely, and slipped a tiny rosebud into her hand. "Godspeed," she whispered, leaving Carly with that last drop of encouragement she needed to follow her heart . . . to Matt.

Images of Matt played over and over in her head, like a broken film . . . a smiling Matt, a loving Matt, then finally a pained Matt walking out of her life a short twenty-four hours before.

Carly's emotions seesawed between joy and sadness, loving exhilaration—and cold fear.

"Hey, lady, want to run by Fisherman's Wharf on the way? It's just a couple blocks west. No trouble. Tourists usually like that stuff—"

"No!" Carly lurched forward and clutched the back of the worn driver's seat. "No, please. You promised to get me there on time!"

"Oh, yeah. Almost forgot. 'Get me to the church on time' . . ." His voice took off on a discordant roller coaster of notes, a lopsided grin on his weathered face. "Sure will, lady, sure will."

He took a sharp left, and sent Carly sliding the length of the back seat. When she managed to straighten her hat back off her eyes, she spied a clock outside a bank on the street they were whizzing by. Eleven forty-five! "Sir," she pleaded, finding his eyes in the mirror, small round eyes softened by dozens of tiny laugh lines. "Sir, do you . . . do you think we'll make it on time?"

He turned halfway around, one arm crooked over the back seat, and winked broadly at Carly. "Lady, I ain't never disappointed a fare yet!"

True to his word, he slammed on the brakes minutes later, bringing the cab to a screeching halt at the top of a curving hilly road. In the distance was the ocean, the rough waves breaking against the harbored shore, sunlight dancing off the crests. To the right, past a narrow border of tall, thin-leafed trees, was a large, stone church, its steeple etched against an intensely blue sky.

"Here you are, Miss Windy City—just like I promised. Ten minutes to spare. Maybe you'll get to meet the bride before the shindig."

Carly tried to swallow around the huge lump that had grown in her throat. "This . . . this is it, then?"

"You got 'er. Holy Angel's it is." He sketched a hasty sign of the cross over his chest before circling the car to open Carly's door. "Now you have a good time. And . . . and I hope you find the lucky guy!" In seconds he was back in the driver's seat and gone, speeding down the steep, twisting hill toward the ocean.

Carly stood there alone at the curb, staring in panic at the vanishing cab. She had an insane urge to call him back, to take him into the church with her, or to hide in the back seat and flee back to the airport and . . . and what? And nothing. Emptiness. Loneliness. No. Never!

Nervously she drew her eyes to tne church. The cab driver had let her off a discreet distance from the entrance, for which she breathed a silent "thank you."

Shoving her hands into the hidden pockets of her full, linen skirt, she paused in the cool shade of a flowering dogwood and watched several small groups of people chattering their way up to the church's entrance. Friends? Relatives? There was so very much she didn't know about this other life of Matt Linton. She squinted against the sun's glare, trying to recognize familiar features on the strangers' faces, but couldn't.

Her stomach began to contract and she felt moisture collect in the palms of her hands. Calm down, Carly West, she scolded herself. It will be all right. Everything will be all right . . . it has to. It was right to come, right to fall in love. . . .

A wide fan of steps led up to two mammoth oak doors, opened wide now, welcoming the festive groups inside.

Carly spotted several clusters of laughing, care-free college-age students. "Tracy's friends," she murmured, and began the long walk past the strangers and up the steps into the damp shadows of the church's vestibule.

She looked about as her eyes adjusted to the dim light. The church was traditional in every way—

large, ornate statues, shiny, polished pews, and the marble altar in the distance, decorated today with huge baskets of multicolored summery flowers. Brilliant, colored rays from the stained-glass windows slanted in on the gathering crowd and Carly smiled for the first time; at least her dress was appropriate. She looked in on everything from pale linen suits to well-worn blue jeans. At least I won't embarrass Matt, she observed. *Matt.* Her heart lurched. Matt. Her eyes darted through and around the patches of color, seeking his face as she became swallowed up in the intense, almost painful, desire to fold him in her arms and press her body to his. She needed him with an intensity that weakened her knees and caused her breath to catch in her throat.

She leaned lightly against a nearby wall, welcoming the support.

"You must be Carly . . ." A soft, precise voice sounded at her elbow.

Carly turned. The woman standing there was about her own height, with gentle, hazel eyes crinkling at the corners into a soft fan of lines. Her auburn hair was cut short and carefully coiffed into soft waves about her attractive face, and the smile that followed her words was warm and welcoming. The woman held out her hand. "I'm so glad you could come."

Carly was silent for a minute, as if adjusting to the moment, finding herself oddly comfortable in the woman's presence. When she spoke her voice was relaxed and familiar. "You're Jenna."

Their smiles melted together and confirmed one another.

"I . . . I hope it was all right. To come, I mean, without any notice—"

Jenna laughed graciously. "Goodness! Carly, this whole wedding had no notice! But I think we've managed to pull it all together. Your being here will mean a lot to Matt."

Carly shifted, her gaze searching Jenna's face, "I'm happy to be here for your daughter's wedding. And about Matt—I . . . I—"

Jenna stepped into the tiny pause. "Matt loves you very much, Carly. I . . . I know it must have been difficult for you to come out here—"

Carly looked down but Jenna continued, "We talked nearly all night, Carly. About the kids, about him. About you. Even about David's surprise visit to Chicago." She touched Carly's arm gently and their eyes met again. "I know you must be filled with a million conflicting emotions. Meeting me. The children. Having Matt's past thrown at you. His life. The way he used to be. But, Carly, don't hold the past against Matt. I don't. My only regret"—her eyes twinkled and she smiled softly—"my only regret is that I didn't meet him now."

"Ah! There you are—"

Carly and Jenna looked up as a dark-suited gentleman with graying temples and a broad smile

178

joined them. He leaned over and kissed Jenna warmly on the lips and Carly noticed Jenna's immediate response.

"Carly, I'd like you to meet my husband, Bill Chapman."

Bill took Carly's hand in a bearlike grip and pumped it enthusiastically. "Great! Pleased to meet you! This is turning into quite a day."

Carly chatted politely and hoped her face didn't register the surprise she was feeling. So Jenna was married. Somehow the thought had never occurred to Carly. With a start she realized she had stagnated Matt's past, attached it like a noose around his neck. Together with all its mistakes and unhappy memories. Jenna's lovely smile and happy face helped to dim that now and Carly was washed with a sweet sensation—a delicious feeling that propelled her thoughts into the future, a future as bright and clear as the sky above.

In the distance the dissonant tuning of strings drew a hush over the crowd in the back of the church. Bill turned to Carly.

"How about if I find you a place and we let the mother of the bride be sure Tracy hasn't traded her gown in for blue jeans while Jenna's back was turned."

"Thank you," Carly answered but her heart was doing somersaults in her chest. She so needed to see Matt, this moment, this instant! She shivered slightly. *Matt, oh, Matt, where are you?*

179

Jenna read her thoughts. "Matt is in the sacristy with Father O'Brian, Carly." Her brows furrowed slightly. "I don't think there's time to take you to him before the ceremony begins—" She looked anxiously over her shoulder at the closed dressing-room door.

"I understand," Carly said softly. "I thought perhaps he'd be walking down the aisle with Tracy—"

Bill spoke, a deep laugh coating his words. "Tracy kind of changed things around on us. She and Scott —that's her husband-to-be—are going to be walking down the aisle together."

Jenna shrugged her slim shoulders and smiled resignedly. "This wedding is definitely a hodge-podge of compromises. But believe it or not, we've all survived with nary a battle scar, and for the first time in years, everyone is speaking to one another." She grinned then with a quick, sure smile that lit her face, and continued, "but Tracy asked Matt to be their best man. She told him that fit best . . ." Jenna's eyes misted noticeably. She dabbed at them and tried to clear her throat of the strain of emotion before going on. "Imagine—her *best* man—after all these years. It meant a lot to him, Carly. . . ."

"And now, my love," Bill stepped in, "you need to be getting back to Tracy."

Jenna nodded. She turned to go, then touched Carly's arm lightly. "But I'll see you after the ceremony, Carly. Bill will take care of you—" And she was gone, her thoughts redirected toward her only daughter waiting behind the closed doors.

Carly and Bill watched the door close, then Carly turned slowly back to the main body of the church. "Bill, if you don't mind, I'd prefer to sit toward the back." She smiled into understanding eyes. "I think I'd be more comfortable."

She settled herself at the end of a crowded pew just as the strings increased in volume. The crowd hushed in anticipation.

Candles were lit on the altar and shadows filled the simple sanctuary as several figures emerged from the sacristy door.

A gasp slipped from Carly's mouth as she watched the small entourage line the wide steps. An elderly gentleman seated next to her smiled indulgently, offering her his handkerchief. Carly shook her head politely, then her eyes flew back to the altar as a fierce hot joy shot through her.

Matt walked slowly, his tall figure dwarfing the small, gowned prelate. His face was set in a serious expression and his eyes were drawn down the aisle to await the bride. Others moved before him and after him, but all was a blur for Carly save for the strong, pensive face of the man she loved more than life itself. A thick, sweet fire ran through her, running down her limbs and spine and filling her with a nearly unbearable joy.

She truly did love him—without restraints or fears or complications. She was at peace in a fiery flare of passion. Her heart gave a great leap and she yearned for him to see her, to feel her love, to know she was there and was his, if he still wanted her in his life.

Slowly she felt movement and realized the crowd was turning sideways, facing the center aisle. Carly pulled her eyes away from Matt.

Several tanned, youthful women in an assortment of soft summer dresses walked smiling down the aisle. Seconds later the strings broke into a joyful Renaissance dance and Tracy Linton appeared at the back entrance, a handsome, rugged man beside her, both washed in the glow of love.

Tracy's dress was a swirl of cotton and linen and floated down around her ankles in gentle folds. Tiny sprigs of baby's breath were threaded through the dark mass of curls framing her delicate face. Carly's eyes were drawn to her, to the familiar twinkle in her eyes, the ready laughter lurking behind the controlled corners of her mouth. Matt's daughter. Her head turned from side to side as she greeted friends with a smile and drew them into her joy.

And then her eyes met Carly's and held there for a brief moment. Her lips parted and her eyes grew bright in recognition. And then the smile spread, spilling over with the welcoming warmth of happiness.

From the altar Matt watched Tracy's movements and felt an outpouring of love for this rambunctious child who had grown into such a lovely woman—in spite of him. He caught her smile and answered it with a proud, loving smile of his own. His eyes damp, the muscles in his jaw jumping with restrained emotion. In a private signal, his daughter lifted her chin, held his gaze, then tipped her head to the side, telling him something . . . telling him to look . . . to see . . .

Carly! His Carly! His love—sitting there in a wide-brimmed hat and a blouse the color of crushed roses. For that moment he saw her as his daughter must have, a lovely young woman, sitting nervously on the aisle of a back pew at a stranger's wedding— a smile trembling on her lips, her hands folded softly in her lap, her face flushed with hope. And then, as their eyes met, he saw the Carly only he knew. The eager, vibrant woman whose love was a gift beyond all price. The one woman he would cherish for all his life . . . and whose love would cherish and sustain him.

He wanted to leap in the air, shout, dance around the altar. He wanted to run down the aisle and lift her in his arms, his sky gypsy, and fly away. He wanted to cry.

But instead he smiled, and turned for the moment back to the sweet ceremony of his daughter's wedding.

CHAPTER TEN

Matt swung his small car to a stop in the driveway of his house, turned, and caught Carly in his arms with a sheer, trembling joy. "We're here—"

Carly couldn't remember a moment of the wedding, the reception, the drive down the coast to Palo Alto. She was too filled with happiness. She felt as if she had swallowed a balloon; swelling, expanding, her love for Matt grew until she thought she'd burst with the wonder of it. It made her heart ache; it pushed tears to the corners of her eyes and left them balancing there, glistening on her lashes in the California sunlight.

She smiled at him again for the thousandth time, and he laughed.

"You look like a kid on Christmas morning!"

She shook her head. "Happier!" And reaching

over, she ruffled his crisp hair. "So, what has Santa brought me?"

"Hugs and kisses," he answered softly, and catching her smoke-dark hair in one hand at the nape of her neck, he dusted them freely across her upturned face. He held her close, nestled within the curve of his strong arms. "I don't want to ever let you go, Gypsy."

"No . . . never," she agreed, snuggling against him in pure contentment. She rubbed her cheek against his shoulder and looked up at him, her eyes shining with happiness. A small smile twitched the corner of her lips, and she giggled. "I can just see the headlines now, Professor. 'Couple found mummified in car. Embrace lasts centuries'!"

Matt's laughing breath stirred her hair.

"Centuries? Then I've a better idea. Come with me, woman."

With a quick brush of his lips against hers, he slid from the car, raced around to her side, and tugged her back into his arms. They hurried up the front walk, then Carly slowed, resisting the pull of his arm.

"What? What is it, Carly?"

Her dark eyes flicked back and forth across his face. "I want to tell you now, Matt"—she touched his face tenderly—"now, before we get crazy and I'm in your arms and you think it's just my passion talking. Matt Linton, I love you."

All his love was reflected in his eyes as she spoke,

those sky-blue, make-your-dream-come-true blue eyes. He smiled and started to speak, but Carly pressed her fingertips against his lips, silencing him. "No, me first. I love you. Have since the moment I saw you with your pants legs rolled up on the beach. My, you were handsome! And I've loved you through all the craziness. Even when I was trying to put you off, my heart was sure; only my fears—my 'warehouse of hang-ups'—wouldn't let me admit it. And Matt—I'll love you forever. It doesn't matter where we are, what we do. If I can sell kites in Chicago, then heck, I can sell kites along Big Sur . . . !"

He caught her face in his hands, pushing her hair back with both hands as if to draw her whole face into his kiss. "I love *you*, Carly." His voice was husky and low, a sweet whisper on her lips. "I don't know how I got to be so lucky. With you in my life, I wake up every day glad to be alive. Every day is too short; and now every night will be ours. . . . And I've already asked Stanford for a delayed return. Northwestern was more than happy to extend my stay. We can take a year to decide where we want to live and—"

"What? You . . . you presumptuous schemer!" She grinned happily.

"Yes, darling. A man in love is driven to desperate acts. And here comes another. . . ." He covered her lips with his own, and his kiss was only a promise of what was to come. "Will you marry me, Gypsy?"

"Yes, Professor. Yes."

He swept her up into his arms, carried her in through the house and up the stairs.

"Wait! Oh, wait . . . what an incredible view of the ocean, and what beautiful rooms . . . wait, oh put me down . . ."

"No! Sightseeing can wait until later. The view will still be there. Though if I have my way, it will be too dark to see anything but me!" His husky, aroused laugh rumbled against the flattened softness of her breasts trapped there against the curving bow of his chest. He kissed her again, the touch of his tongue exciting her so that she stopped her protests and wound her fingers in his hair.

They fell together onto the bed. His eager hands crushed the dusty-rose blouse, tossed off her linen skirt. Her adoring hands urged him out of his clothes and caressed his flesh. They tumbled together, meeting, fusing, their bodies yearning for the physical affirmation of their love.

"I love you . . . love you, Matt," Carly whispered as he stroked and petted her, sending her senses whirling. "I love you."

"And I love you, my dearest, darling sky gypsy," he answered, his lips and fingertips adoring her.

With an aching feeling of abandon, a voluptuous softening of all parts of her body, her heart beating with joy at fulfilled love, Carly welcomed him. And Matt, his body perfectly matched to hers, at once consumed and heightened her passion. Her breasts rose with a great deep breath of joy, and she heard him cry her name and felt his body tense and gather and surge . . . and she, with little cries of love, met the great cresting wave of his passion and they peaked and crashed together onto a silver shore. . . .

Outside, waves that were only water did crash and tumble on a real beach. The house sat quietly perched above it. And no one would have guessed the love that soared within.

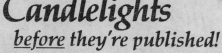

All-new Candlelight Newsletter

An exceptional, _free_ offer awaits readers of Dell's incomparable Candlelight Ecstasy and Supreme Romances.

Subscribe to our all-new CANDLELIGHT NEWSLETTER and you will receive—at absolutely no cost to you—exciting, exclusive information about today's finest romance novels and novelists. You'll be part of a select group to receive sneak previews of upcoming Candlelight Romances, well in advance of publication.

You'll also go behind the scenes to "meet" our Ecstasy and Supreme authors, learning firsthand where they get their ideas and how they made it to the top. News of author appearances and events will be detailed, as well. And contributions from the Candlelight editor will give you the inside scoop on how she makes her decisions about what to publish—and how _you_ can try your hand at writing an Ecstasy or Supreme.

You'll find all this and more in Dell's CANDLELIGHT NEWSLETTER. And best of all, _it costs you nothing._ That's right! It's Dell's way of thanking our loyal Candlelight readers and of adding another dimension to your reading enjoyment.

Just fill out the coupon below, return it to us, and look forward to receiving the first of many CANDLELIGHT NEWSLETTERS—overflowing with the kind of excitement that only enhances our romances!

 DELL READERS SERVICE-Dept. B602B
P.O. BOX 1000, PINE BROOK, N.J. 07058

Name_____

Address_____

City_____

State_____ Zip_____

Candlelight
Ecstasy Romances™

$1.95 each

At your local bookstore or use this handy coupon for ordering:

 Dell | **DELL BOOKS—Dept. B602C**
P.O. BOX 1000, PINE BROOK, N.J. 07058-1000

Please send me the books I have checked above. I am enclosing $ _____ [please add 75c per copy to cover postage and handling]. Send check or money order—no cash or C.O.D.'s. Please allow up to 8 weeks for shipment.

Name _____

Address _____

City _____ State/Zip _____